QUEST

A SCHOLASTIC
READING
IMPROVEMENT
SERIES

JUST A MATTER OF TIME

AND OTHER STORIES

Program Consultants:

MARK W. AULLS, ED.D
McGILL UNIVERSITY

MICHAEL F. GRAVES, PH.D.
UNIVERSITY OF MINNESOTA

SCHOLASTIC INC.

THE QUEST STAFF

Curriculum Consultants:
Patricia Collins, Mary Haynes and Nedra West
  New Orleans Effective Schools Project
  New Orleans, Louisiana

Rene Sheldon
  La Mesa-Spring Valley School District
  La Mesa, California

Project Editor: Adrienne Betz

Editors: John Albin, Lucy Straus

Editorial Director: Eleanor Angeles

Art Direction: Michaelis/Carpelis Design

Contributing Editor: Adrian Peetoom

Grateful acknowledgement is made to the following authors and publishers for the use of copyrighted materials. Every effort has been made to obtain permission to use previously published material. Any errors or omissions are unintentional.

Macmillan Publishing Company for "Sunset: St. Louis" from COLLECTED POEMS OF SARA TEASDALE. Copyright 1920 by Macmillan Publishing Company, renewed 1948 by Mamie T. Wheless.

Charles Scribner's Sons for "Children of the Desert" from THE DESERT IS THEIRS by Byrd Baylor. Copyright © 1975 by Byrd Baylor.

Scholastic Inc. for "Starlight, Starbright." Copyright © 1973 by Scholastic Inc.

Alfred A. Knopf for "My Kind of Watch," adapted from "Father Teaches Me to be Prompt" from LIFE WITH FATHER by Clarence Day. Copyright 1935 by Clarence Day and renewed 1963 by Mrs. Katherine B. Day.

Alfred A. Knopf for "Amigo Brothers" from STORIES FROM EL BARRIO by Piri Thomas. Copyright © 1978 by Piri Thomas.

Dodd, Mead & Company for adaptation of "Randy" from THE DINGLE RIDGE FOX AND OTHER STORIES by Sam Savitt. Copyright © 1978 by Sam Savitt.

Laurel G. Sherman for "The Cold Winds of Summer," adapted from "June 1816 We Almost Froze to Death." Copyright © 1984 by Open Court Publishing.

Alfred Slote for "The Willing." Copyright © 1985 by Alfred Slote.

The Putnam Publishing Group for "Butterflies" from ON THE ROAD WITH CHARLES KURALT by Charles Kuralt. Copyright © 1985 by CBS, Inc.

Coward, McCann & Geoghegan for "Susan's Trial" from MOTHER, AUNT SUSAN AND ME by William Jay Jacobs. Copyright © 1979 by William Jay Jacobs.

Patricia Lauber for adaptation from CLARENCE TURNS SEA DOG. Copyright © 1959 by Patricia Lauber.

Scholastic Inc. for adaptation of "The Secret Plan" from ADVENTURES OF THE RED TAPE GANG. Copyright © 1974 by Joan Lowery Nixon.

Martin Tahse Productions for the adaptation of "Just a Matter of Time," a teleplay by Paul W. Cooper, based on the JUST A MATTER OF TIME by Roni Schotter.

Penguin Books Ltd. for adaptation of "The Strange Illness of Mr. Arthur Cook" from THE SHADOW CAGE AND OTHER TALES OF THE SUPERNATURAL by Philippa Pearce. Copyright © 1977 by Philippa Pearce.

Harper & Row, Publishers, Inc. for adaptation of "The Strange Illness of Mr. Arthur Cook" from THE SHADOW CAGE AND OTHER TALES OF THE SUPERNATURAL by Philippa Pearce. Copyright © 1977 by Philippa Pearce.

The New York Times for adaptation of "About New York: Licensed to Prune: A Corps of Ardent Tree Lovers" by William E. Geist. Copyright © 1986 by The New York Times.

North Point Press for adaptation from "He Was a Good Lion" from WEST WITH THE WIND by Beryl Markham. Copyright © 1983 by Beryl Markham.

The Wall Street Journal for adaptation of "Odd Things Happen Like Toad Showers and Psychic Feelings" by Barry Newman. Copyright © 1986 by Dow Jones & Company.

William Morrow & Company for adaptation from RICH MITCH by Marjorie Weinman Sharmat. Copyright © 1983 by Marjorie Weinman Sharmat.

Little, Brown and Company for adaptation of "Nature's Amazing Clocks" from THIS BOOK IS ABOUT TIME by Marilyn Burns. Copyright © 1978 by the Yolla Bolly Press.

William Morrow & Company for "The Third Jump," adapted from "Open Letter to a Young Negro" from BLACKTHINK by Jesse Owens with Paul G. Neimark. Copyright © 1970 by Jesse Owens and Paul G. Neimark.

Lothrop, Lee & Shepard, a division of William Morrow & Company for "The Women's 400 Meter" from THE SIDEWALK RACER AND OTHER POEM OF SPORTS AND MOTION by Lillian Morrison. Copyright © 1968 by Lillian Morrison.

Doubleday & Company, Inc. for "Direction" by Alonzo Lopez from THE WHISPERING WIND, edited by Terry Allen. Copyright © 1972 by The Institute of American Indian Arts.

Ecco Press for "Portrait" from DESCENDING FIGURE by Louise Gluck. Copyright © 1976, 1977, 1978, 1979, 1980 by Louise Gluck.

Harper & Row, Publishers, Inc. for "There Isn't Time" from ELEANOR FARJEON'S POEMS FOR CHILDREN. Copyright © 1933, 1961 by Eleanor Farjeon.

Harper & Row, Publishers, Inc. for "Marie Lucille" from BRONZEVILLE BOYS AND GIRLS by Gwendolyn Brooks. Copyright © 1956 by Gwendolyn Brooks Blakely.

Editor of *Poetry* and Constance Urdang for "Pole Vault" by Shiro Murano, translated by Satoru Sato and Constance Urdang. Copyright © 1956 by The Modern Poetry Association.

ILLUSTRATION AND PHOTOGRAPHY: Gary Ciccarelli: cover; Don Almquist: 13, 23, 29, 35, 55, 67, 83, 97, 107, 113, 119, 145, 153, 161, 169, 189, 291, 209, 217, 235, 245, 257, 269; Animals Animals/Carson Baldwin, Jr.: 163; Animals Animals/E. R. Degginger: 165; Animals Animals/Stouffer Productions: 162; Donna Ayers: 30–31, 171, 175, 177; David Celsi: 246–248, 252; Focus On Sports: 227–228; Paul Frame: 47, 148; Keith Kohler: 90, 108; Armen Kojoyian: 98, 100, 103, 137; Ray Lago: 211–212; Narda Lebo: 114–115, 182; Bryce Lee: 282; Tom Lulavitch: 259–260, 264, 270–271; Frank Mayo: 281; B. G. Murray, Jr.: 25; Patti Murray: 24–25; Anne Neuman: 89; Jürg Obrist: 146–147, 149; Oxford Scientific Films: 24; Dario Perla/International Stock Photography: 48; Ralph A. Reinhold: 24; Anne Rich: 154–155, 157, 181, 203, 205; Roger Roth: 218, 221–222, 236, 239, 241; John Sanford: 36, 38, 40, 42, 190, 192, 195, 197; Jeffrey Smith: 69, 71, 73, 75, 79; Leslie Stall: 120, 124, 127, 130–132; Lynn Stone: 25; Arthur Thompson: 84–85; Neil Waldman: 57–59, 61, 63

ISBN 0-590-34975-9 (Softcover Edition)

Copyright © 1987 by Scholastic Inc. All rights reserved. Published by Scholastic Inc.
12 11 10 9 8 7 6 5 4 3 2 1   7   8 9/8 0/1/9

Printed in the U.S.A.

UNIT
2

A HELPING HAND

UNIT INTRODUCTION   52

The Third Jump
by Jesse Owens and
Paul Neimark   54

In the 1936 Olympic Games, Jesse Owens faced an unusual challenge. Read this story to find out who gave Jesse Owens the help he needed.

Reading and Vocabulary Skills   64

The Secret Plan
by Joan Lowry Nixon   66

Michael and his friends think their new club should do something to help the city. Find out what happens when they set out to do their first good deed.

Reading and Vocabulary Skills   80

The Friends of Trees
by William E. Geist   82

Why do some people cut branches off trees? You'll find the answer in the article.

Reading and Vocabulary Skills   86

Poems About A Helping Hand   88

Portrait
by Louise Gluck

Direction
by Alonzo Lopez

Reading and Vocabulary Skills   91

UNIT REVIEW   92

UNIT

3

SOMETHING STRANGE

UNIT INTRODUCTION   94

**The Willing
by Alfred Slote**   96

Robbie thinks he can will things to happen, or not to happen. Read this story to find out about the strange things that happen to Robbie.

Reading and Vocabulary Skills   104

**The Cold Winds of Summer
by L. G. Sherman**   106

1816 has been called "the year without a summer." Read this article to find out what happened and why, when the cold winds blew.

Reading and Vocabulary Skills   110

**Odd Things Happen
by Barry Newman**   112

Robert Rickard looks into strange events that seem impossible to explain. As you read the article, decide how you will explain the odd things that happen.

Reading and Vocabulary Skills   116

**The Strange Illness of
Mr. Arthur Cook
by Philippa Pearce**   118

Shortly after the Cook family move into their new home, Mr. Cook comes down with a mysterious illness. His daughter Judy searches to find the explanation.

Reading and Vocabulary Skills   134

Poems About Something Strange   136

There Was a Young Lady of Lynn
Anonymous

Sam
by Walter De La Mare

Reading and Vocabulary Skills   139

UNIT REVIEW   140

UNIT
4

IT'S ABOUT TIME

UNIT INTRODUCTION   142

Lucky Break
by Adrienne Popper   144

Can Toby Fancher get through the whole day without Hulk Horgan getting to him? It's a question of timing, and all Toby needs is a lucky break.

Reading and Vocabulary Skills   150

My Kind of Watch
by Clarence Day   152

Clarence's father thinks it's important for Clarence to be on time, but, somehow, Clarence is always late. Maybe a watch will help—if it's the right kind of watch.

Reading and Vocabulary Skills   158

Nature's Amazing Clocks
by Marilyn Burns   160

Many animals have their own ways of keeping time. Read this article to find out some of the things scientists have found out about the things animals can do.

Reading and Vocabulary Skills   166

Just a Matter of Time
by Paul W. Cooper   168

This play shows what one girl learns about herself when she has to face the changes time brings into her life.

Reading and Vocabulary Skills   178

Poems About It's About Time   180

Marie Lucille
by Gwendolyn Brooks

There Isn't Time
by Eleanor Farjeon

Reading and Vocabulary Skills   183

UNIT REVIEW   184

UNIT 5

WINNING AND LOSING

UNIT INTRODUCTION   186

**The Grand Prize
by Marjorie Weinman
Sharmat**   188

Mitch's hobby is entering contests.
He never wins anything, until, one
day, a phone call changes everything.

Reading and Vocabulary Skills   198

**A Private Place
by Phyllis Fair Cowell**   200

When Beth's grandfather comes to
live with her family, and take over
her room, Beth is ready to put up a
fight. Read to find out what Beth
learns about winning and losing
when she loses her "private place."

Reading and Vocabulary Skills   206

**Aunt Susan's Trial
by William Jay Jacobs**   208

In 1872, Susan B. Anthony was
arrested and tried because she voted
in an election. This is the story of her
trial, told by Harriot Stanton, who
was 16 years old at the time.

Reading and Vocabulary Skills   214

**Amigo Brothers
by Piri Thomas**   216

What will happen when two best
friends must meet in the boxing
ring? Find out how Felix and Antonio
meet the greatest challenge of their
lives in this exciting story.

Reading and Vocabulary Skills   224

Poems About Winning and Losing   226

The Women's 400 Meters
by Lillian Morrison

Pole Vault
by Shiro Murano

Reading and Vocabulary Skills   229

UNIT REVIEW   230

UNIT
6
TIGHT SPOTS

UNIT INTRODUCTION   232

**He Was a Good Lion
by Beryl Markham**   234

Beryl Markham grew up in Africa in the 1900's. In this true story, she tells what happens when she comes face to face with a lion.

Reading and Vocabulary Skills   242

**Buried Treasure
by Patricia Lauber**   244

Speed Armstrong doesn't think Pat and Brian's dog Clarence can find buried treasure. Read this story to find out why Speed changes his mind about Clarence.

Reading and Vocabulary Skills   254

**The Thinking Machine
by Jacques Futrelle**   256

Professor Van Dusen is known as "The Thinking Machine" because of his great mental powers. In this story, which is told in two parts, The Thinking Machine decides to prove that he can think his way out of anything—even a prison cell.

PART 1

Reading and Vocabulary Skills   266

The Thinking Machine, Part 2   268

Reading And Vocabulary Skills   278

Poems About Tight Spots   280

The Shark
By Lord Alfred Douglas

A Narrow Fellow in the Grass
by Emily Dickinson

Be Like the Bird
by Victor Hugo

Reading and Vocabulary Skills   283

UNIT REVIEW   284

GLOSSARY   286

UNIT

·1·

HOMEBASE

Almost everyone has a homebase. In this unit, you will find that a "homebase" can be many different things. It can be your home or a special place away from your usual home. It can be a place to search for, a place to return to, a place to remember. The selections in this unit show that people are not the only ones to seek a homebase.

In the story "Claire's Cousin from Cairo," Lisa is excited by the idea of meeting someone whose home is far away from hers. She may learn more about Cairo that she even imagined. The article "The Butterfly Mystery" describes the surprising flights of the monarch butterflies every year. You'll find out why some people think their flight is an event beyond explanation. The story "Starlight, Starbright" explains why Lacy's ideas about home are so different from those of her parents and brother. "Randy's Journey" is the story of a golden dog whose long journey takes him to many homes and many people. His homebase turns out to be the one where he is most loved and needed.

The two poems that end this unit, "Children of the Desert" and "Sunset (St. Louis)," show two very different kinds of homebases. One describes his life in the desert, and in the other a famous poet tells about her favorite time in her home city.

Each selection in this unit is about a different kind of homebase. As you read you may find that a homebase is not always the same. It can be any place where you truly feel at home.

UNDERSTANDING WORDS IN SENTENCES

Words about a Homebase. Certain words can help you understand what it means to leave one homebase and look for another. Six of those words are in bold print in the sentences below. All the words are used in this unit.

Use the rest of each sentence to help you choose the correct meaning of each word in **bold print**. Then write the word and its meaning on your paper.

1. Lisa had a strong desire to **explore** places in other countries.
   (travel to learn or to discover, speak another language)

2. In the spring, thousands of butterflies **migrate** from California to Canada.
   (travel from one area to another, change size and color)

3. "Growing a crop in a tank of water is not farming," his father **exploded.**
   (said angrily, admitted secretly)

4. Randy trotted to the end of the driveway but he never **roamed** away from the house until spring.
   (ran after bicycles, wandered around)

5. Mr. Radcliff was more interested in **possessing** dogs than in loving them.
   (showing, owning)

6. Before long, Randy had become a **drifter,** making only a few visits to his old home.
   (one who moves about without purpose, one who floats on the water)

◆ INTRODUCING ◆
"CLAIRE'S COUSIN FROM CAIRO"

Lisa can hardly wait to meet Claire's cousin from Cairo. After all, she has never met anyone from a foreign country. Besides, her own hometown could certainly use some excitement. Lisa describes the events that lead to the visit from Claire's cousin. Find out what changes will take place in Lisa's own life.

WORDS TO KNOW

The words in **bold print** are from "Claire's Cousin From Cairo." Study each word and its meaning carefully.

Lisa expected Claire's cousin to look **exotic,** like girls from foreign countries.
   exotic — interestingly different

Claire's favorite sport in school was **lacrosse.**
   lacrosse — a ball game played with long sticks

Claire seemed to have better **coordination** than the other players on the team.
   coordination — ability to move smoothly

When Lisa thought of Egypt, she pictured the hot sandy deserts and **pyramids** she had learned about.

   pyramids — triangular shaped buildings used as tombs for rulers of ancient Egypt

Claire's cousin spoke with a soft **accent.**
   accent — a manner of speaking that is typical of a region or foreign country

An **atlas** gave Lisa some information about Cairo that she didn't expect to find.
   atlas — book of maps

Lisa wondered if life **abroad** was more exciting than life in America.
   abroad — away from home, away from one's home country

CLAIRE'S COUSIN FROM CAIRO

by JOHANNA HURWITZ

The whole thing started with a lunch-time conversation. I sit at the same table in the cafeteria every day with the same ninth-grade friends, but there are usually a few girls at the other end of the table that I don't hang around with. I was sitting and talking with Meredith and Hillary and Gina. Gina had been out sick with the flu all last week, and she was filling us in on the TV soaps — who was marrying whom and all the usual things that happen on soap operas. Fortunately, or maybe unfortunately, I hadn't been sick all year. So I'd lost touch with the TV soaps, and I wasn't paying much attention to the conversation.

That's why I caught what Claire Shay said to her friends at the other end of the table.

"My cousin from Cairo is coming to visit here at Thanksgiving."

The word *Cairo* caught my attention. We had been studying the Middle East in social studies. It's not my favorite subject. All those foreign countries are so far away, they seem unreal. Yet, here was Claire Shay, who had been in classes with me for years and years, having relatives in Cairo, Egypt. I was amazed. My relatives are very boring and live, like me, in ordinary places.

I couldn't ask Claire straight out about her cousin. After all, even though we were in the same gym class, I don't think I had spoken to her for two years. But I kept thinking about her cousin. I wondered what she would be like. I was curious to meet someone who lived in Cairo.

It was not until a couple of days later that I managed, accidentally-on-purpose, to meet Claire as we were leaving school. I usually take the bus, but I had offered to pick up some vitamins for my mother at the drug-

13

store near the school. The store just happened to be near Claire's home, too.

"Hi," I called out to her. "Wait up."

I suspect that she was surprised to have me greet her. But she didn't let on, and we walked along together.

"Only another week to Thanksgiving," I said to her.

"Yeah," she agreed.

Since she didn't volunteer that her cousin was coming, I tried again.

"Are you doing anything special for the holiday?"

"Just eating turkey," she said. "What else do you do on Thanksgiving?"

Boy, was she being difficult. "We usually have some relatives over," I said.

"Same thing here," she said.

I didn't know why she wasn't talking about her cousin from Cairo. But the less she said, the more I wanted to know.

"Maybe we could get together and do something that weekend," I suggested. I couldn't remember the last time Claire Shay and I had done something together. I think it was in sixth grade, when we were both invited to the same birthday party.

We were almost at the drugstore. I had to decide quickly if it was worth my while to walk past it so I could spend more time with Claire. Just as I made up my mind to continue walking with her, Claire said, "I've got to pick up some shampoo." She turned into the drugstore.

"I'm stopping here, too," I said, and followed her inside. The vitamins were near

the front, and the shampoo was in another part of the store.

"See you, Lisa," Claire said.

"Right," I agreed. I grabbed the vitamins and waited near the checkout until Claire came.

"We meet again," I said.

We paid for our purchases and left the store together.

This is ridiculous, I thought. Being subtle doesn't work.

"I heard you say at lunch the other day that you have a cousin who lives in Cairo."

"Yeah," Claire said.

"Have you ever visited her?" I asked.

"No," Claire said.

"Too bad," I said. "It must be interesting to explore other places and see different lifestyles."

"It's not that different from here," said Claire, shrugging her shoulders.

I remembered that Mrs. Hillman, my sociology teacher, had said that American movies and rock music were popular in many other countries. She said that lots of people dressed the way we did, too. Still, there had to be some differences.

"How come your cousin lives there?" I asked.

"My uncle works for a big company, and that's where he was assigned," said Claire.

"Do they ever come here?" I asked.

Now she would have to answer me outright!

"Sometimes," Claire said. "My cousin is coming for Thanksgiving."

"Hey, neat!" I said, pretending to be surprised. Of course, if I had heard her say that she had a cousin who lives in Cairo, then I would have heard her say that the cousin was coming for Thanksgiving. But at the moment, I forgot about that and I hoped Claire did, too.

"How old is she? What's her name?" I asked.

"She's almost 15, and her name is Jane."

Jane? I thought she would have an exotic name like Fatima or Farrah.

"Listen," I said. "I'd really like to meet your cousin when she's here. Let's plan to do something together. Okay?"

And then, before Claire could disagree or say anything, I turned in the direction of my house. "See you at school," I called as I walked off.

As a result of our after-school talk, Claire edged herself a couple of places closer to me at the lunch table the next day. And in gym, when we were told to get a partner to practice catching balls with the lacrosse sticks, I edged over to Claire instead of Gina, with whom I usually paired off. Claire's got better coordination than Gina, and instead of spending half the period waiting for her to pick the ball up off the floor, we had a good workout.

"When is your cousin Jane arriving?" I asked, as I cradled the ball.

"Her plane gets in Wednesday evening," Claire said.

I could hardly wait to meet this cousin from Cairo.

My cousins, aunts, uncles, and grandparents all came for dinner on Thanksgiving. One cousin is nine, like my brother. The other is a girl of four. Boring! We ate turkey and gossiped about other relatives, and the day passed as always. Friday, I went over to Claire's house.

"This is Jane," she said, introducing me to her cousin, who was tall and blonde. At first I was disappointed that Jane didn't look more exotic. I guess I thought she would have dark eyes and resemble Elizabeth Taylor as Cleopatra. I saw the movie just a couple of weeks ago on television. Still, I thought to myself, those blue eyes of hers have seen pyramids and mummies and all sorts of exciting things.

"Hi," Jane said. Her voice had a slight drawl.

"I brought my ice skates in case you want to go skating," I said.

"We don't go ice-skating where I live," Jane smiled. "It's too hot."

"Oh, right," I said. I had been too dumb to think of that. I was impressed that Jane's English was so great.

I put my skates down and took off my jacket. "Tell me what it's like where you live,"

I said. "I think it's fantastic that you live in Cairo. It must be so much more interesting than here."

"It's all right," said Jane. "I like it. The kids are okay."

"What kinds of things do you do?"

Jane began talking about her school. She seemed to be studying all the same things that Claire and I were. I loved her voice. It was soft, and the words slid together. I decided that as soon as I got home, I would try to talk like that. I would certainly surprise everyone if I developed an Egyptian accent.

"What's the food like in Cairo?" I asked. I remembered the *falafel* and *pita* bread that we had eaten in class when we completed the unit on the Middle East.

"We have all the same fast-food chains that you do," Jane laughed.

"No kidding?" I was really surprised about that.

It was so interesting talking with Jane that the time really flew. Claire's mother served us turkey sandwiches for lunch. It was exactly what I would have had if I had been home. "Do you want to go to a movie or something?" I suggested when we finished eating.

However, when we took out the newspaper to see what was playing, Jane had seen all the films.

"That's incredible," I said. She was more up to date on things than I was. I decided that they must release some of the movies abroad before they even showed them in this country.

In the end, we decided to just walk down to the mall and look around. Claire was

looking bored, but I thought that I could spend hours with Jane and not get tired. I felt as if some of her exotic, foreign life was rubbing off on me.

It was cold out, but not windy. "It's too cold for poor old me," drawled Jane.

I thought of the hot sands in the desert, of camels walking down roads, of the Nile River and the Sphinx (all of which I had seen in a film in social studies).

Claire's cousin sure was lucky! Why couldn't I live in some exciting place like Cairo? How much more fun to wake up in Cairo or Paris or London than to be in

Woodside, New Jersey. There's nothing we did that afternoon, walking through the mall and stopping for hot chocolate, that I hadn't done dozens of other times with Meredith and Hillary and Gina. But, somehow, seeing everything through Jane's eyes made it much more fun.

"This is a nice place to live," said Jane, licking the chocolate from her upper lip. "You're lucky to live here."

"Lucky? Nothing ever happens here," I complained. I thought about how Cairo was in the news lots of times. Whoever heard of Woodside? ·

"Do you play on any teams?" Jane asked. "I'm hoping to get on the girls' basketball team," she said.

"I was thinking about trying out for lacrosse," Claire announced. "What about you, Lisa?" she asked, turning to me. "Why don't you try out, too?"

"I'm not good enough," I said.

"Sure you are," Claire protested. "I saw the way you handled that lacrosse stick in gym. And you're fast, too."

"Really?" I asked. "Do you think I could make the team?"

"I think we both could," said Claire. "And I think it would be loads of fun."

The idea really appealed to me. Neither Meredith, nor Hillary, nor Gina cared much about sports. They preferred to sit around and cheer while the boys shot baskets or hit softballs. Usually, I just sat around with them.

I went home that afternoon feeling good. Jane left the next morning to spend the day in New York City before flying home again on Sunday. It seemed a very short visit to make after such a long flight here. I assumed that her parents had piles of money and could afford to let her fly halfway across the world just for the weekend. I said she was lucky and I was right!

But here's the funny thing: One day several weeks later, when Claire and I were practicing for the lacrosse tryouts together, I asked her if she had heard from her cousin, Jane, lately.

"My mom spoke to her mother on the phone last night," she said.

"That must be very exciting to speak to someone so far away on the telephone," I said.

Claire looked at me as if I were crazy. "Haven't you ever had a long-distance phone call?" she asked.

"Well, sure," I said. "My grandparents phone from Florida to wish me happy birthday every year. But that's not the same thing."

"Why not?"

"Well, there's the big time difference, for one thing," I said. "How can you compare talking to someone in Miami, Florida, with talking to someone in Cairo, Egypt?"

"Cairo, Egypt?" Claire began to laugh. She laughed so hard she could hardly stand up and the lacrosse ball fell out of the pocket in her stick and rolled across the gym floor. "Cairo, Egypt. Cairo, Egypt," she kept saying, almost choking with laughter.

"Yeah. Cairo, Egypt," I said, not understanding what was so funny.

"My cousin, Jane, lives in Cairo, Georgia,"

she gasped out between bursts of laughter.

That night, I looked in the atlas we have at home. I discovered that there is a Cairo, Georgia, and a Cairo, Illinois, as well as the one in Egypt that we learned about in school. Then I discovered that there are eight cities named Paris in the United States, and three cities named London. I don't want to make that kind of mistake again.

So, Claire's cousin was just an ordinary American girl like me. She didn't live an exotic life in a foreign country at all. If she went to my school, she would blend in with all the others. And yet, if I hadn't heard Claire mention her cousin from Cairo, I would never have gotten to know Claire better.

Yesterday, Ms. Aldrich watched as Claire and I were practicing the lacrosse moves. "You girls are both great," she said. "You will be a real asset to the team."

It's going to be an exciting spring, even here in Woodside, New Jersey. ◆

READING CHECK

Answer the following questions about "Claire's Cousin From Cairo." You may want to check your answers by reviewing details in the story.

1. How did Lisa find out that Claire's cousin was coming to visit? Why did the word "Cairo" catch her attention?

2. Why did Lisa want to meet Claire's cousin?

3. What was Lisa's reaction when she learned the name of Claire's cousin? What did she tell Claire she would like to do? What did Lisa think about Jane's appearance when she met her?

4. Why was Lisa surprised to hear what Jane did in Cairo, and what foods she ate there?

5. What did Jane think about life in Lisa's hometown?

6. How did Lisa find out that Jane did not live in Cairo, Egypt? What did she do to check the information?

7. At the end of the story, how did Lisa feel about Claire? How did she feel about her hometown?

WHAT DO YOU THINK?

1. Why do you think meeting someone from a foreign country was so important to Lisa? Would you feel the same way about the opportunity to meet a foreign visitor? Explain why or why not.

2. Lisa may have made a mistake about Cairo, but she made a new friend. Do you think Lisa and Claire would have become friends if Lisa hadn't been so curious? Explain why or why not.

3. Did you guess that Jane was not from Eygpt before Lisa learned the truth? If so, explain how you guessed it.

VOCABULARY CHECK

Read the following sentences and choose the correct meaning of each word in **bold print.** Then write each word and its meaning on your paper.

1. Jane's **accent** was music to Lisa's ears.
   (manner of dressing, manner of talking)

2. Claire and Lisa spent extra time practicing their **lacrosse** moves.
   (ball game, dance steps)

3. Traveling **abroad** can help you learn about different ways of life.
   (away from one's home country, on a wide-bodied airplane)

4. Lisa had been hoping to hear about the **exotic** life Jane led in Cairo.
   (interestingly different, very exciting)

5. Playing team sports well requires plenty of **coordination.**
   (team spirit, smooth movement)

6. A travel book about Egypt would probably contain pictures of **pyramids.**
   (palaces, tombs)

7. An **atlas** is a good place to begin a study of your own hometown.
   (book of photos, book of maps)

STRATEGY CHECK

The paragraph below is based on the story "Claire's Cousin from Cairo." Choose the correct word to fill in each blank. Use the rest of the paragraph and your knowledge of the story to help you. The write the whole paragraph on your paper.

When Lisa tried to make fr___ with Claire, she had a reason. She w___ to meet Claire's cousin from Cairo. The meeting took pl___ at Claire's house. Lisa was s___ that Jane didn't look more exotic. Jane's v___ had a slight drawl. Jane did not seem to think that her own l___ was more exciting than Lisa's.

◆ INTRODUCING ◆
"THE BUTTERFLY MYSTERY"

Every spring, monarch butterflies leave their home in California and fly thousands of miles into Canada. The butterflies travel through storms and across mountains. How do they survive their long journey? You'll find out more about these beautiful creatures in this article.

WORDS TO KNOW

The words in **bold print** are from "The Butterfly Mystery." Study each word and its meaning carefully.

Few people would expect that **fragile** butterflies could survive a journey of two thousand miles.
    fragile — delicate, easily broken

The **offspring** of the butterflies come to the same trees their parents leave.
    offspring — those descended from others, children

The long flight of the butterflies is an unusual act of **navigation.**
    navigation — traveling a route, finding one's way

The people of Pacific Grove show great **affection** for butterflies.
    affection — fondness, love

The butterflies may never **reveal** their secrets, even to scientists.
    reveal — make known

Monarch butterflies are so interesting that they are often studied by **biologists.**
    biologists — scientists who study animals and plants

THE BUTTERFLY MYSTERY

by CHARLES KURALT

Monarch butterflies spend the winter in Pacific Grove, California. In early spring, the monarchs migrate north. This fact is part of a mystery that suggests all kinds of troubling questions.

In the first place, the monarchs are confused by radio, television, and radar waves. And they are destroyed by fertilizer, insect sprays, and air pollution. So how do they survive at all?

In the second place, after they leave Pacific Grove, they fly as far as 2,000 miles into Canada. They fly through storms and across mountains and deserts, even though they are as fragile as feathers. How do they do it?

In the third place, these butterflies do not live long enough to return to Pacific Grove. In the fall, their offspring, who were born in Canada, will come to the very same trees their parents left. How do butterflies, who've never been there, find their way each year?

All of these are good questions to consider. I put some questions about the monarchs to one of Pacific Grove's butterfly lovers.

"How do you explain the affection between Pacific Grove and butterflies?" I asked.

"Well, there are some Indian tales about it," said the butterfly lover. "Every fall when Indian children saw the great golden butterflies, they sang: 'They have come, they have come, bringing peace and bringing plenty.' People in Pacific Grove still think the monarchs are a sign of good fortune. Besides that, they're beautiful."

"And isn't it against the law to harm

one?" I asked.

"Yes. The penalty is a 500-dollar fine and six months in jail. This is a city that loves fragile, beautiful creatures, and we protect them by law."

"How do the butterflies know where to come back to?" I asked.

"Nobody knows," answered the butterfly lover. "It's a kind of miracle. It makes you believe that things are going to go on and on. It's something we can't understand, yet it's delightful to think about."

Pacific Grove celebrates its miracle on private walls and public streets. I found a bulky monument to the monarchs and a wreath bidding them farewell. I even found a little girl running after the butterflies. She did not want to harm them, but she did want to meet one. She never really did, but she shouldn't feel too badly about that. The monarchs don't always reveal their secrets to biologists, either. They are bright, lacy mysteries, and they are very hard to get to know. ◆

READING CHECK

Answer the following questions about "The Butterfly Mystery." You may want to check your answers by reviewing details in the story.

1. In what season do the monarch butterflies leave Pacific Grove? Where do they go from Pacific Grove?

2. What three things can confuse the monarchs on their flight? What three things can harm them?

3. Which butterflies return to Pacific Grove in the fall? Why don't the original butterflies come back?

4. How do people in Pacific Grove seem to feel about the monarchs? How did the first stories about them begin?

5. How are monarch butterflies protected in Pacific Grove? What is the punishment for harming one?

WHAT DO YOU THINK?

1. Do you think that laws to protect butterflies are needed? Explain why, or why not? If you lived in a place where butterflies spent the winter, what might you do to help protect them?

2. What answer could there be to the mystery of the monarchs' long flight to Pacific Grove every year?

3. What do you think people can learn from watching butterflies?

VOCABULARY CHECK

Read the following sentences and choose the correct meaning of each word in **bold print.** Then write each word and its meaning on your paper.

1. **Biologists** who study the flight of the butterflies hope to understand it someday.
   (scientists who study living things, butterfly catchers)

2. The wings of monarch butterflies are as **fragile** as feathers.
   (beautiful, delicate)

3. The butterflies cannot fly back to Pacific Grove but their **offspring** return to the same trees.
   (descendants, travelers)

4. The 2,000-mile journey has been called a miracle of **navigation.**
   (landing on a tree, traveling a route)

5. It may be unusual to have **affection** for butterflies, but not in Pacific Grove.
   (fondness, amusement)

6. The laws passed to protect the butterflies **reveal** how people feel about these beautiful insects.
   (write out, make known)

STRATEGY CHECK

The paragraph below is based on the article "The Butterfly Mystery." Choose the correct word to fill in each blank. Use the rest of the paragraph and your knowledge of the article to help you. Then write the whole paragraph on your paper.

   Monarch butterflies migrate north to Canada every spr____. Somehow, they survive the 2,000-mile long fl____. The next year, their offspring r____ to the same trees and fields. Their return raises many kinds of qu____ for scientists. The people in Pacific Grove love to watch the butterflies, and they pr____ them with laws against harming them.

"STARLIGHT, STARBRIGHT"

Lacy's father had grown up in a different kind of world. It was a world she would never really understand. Read carefully to find the clues that will help you guess the surprise ending of this story, and to discover why Lacy can never understand fully what her father's childhood home was like.

WORDS TO KNOW

The words in **bold print** are from "Starlight, Starbright." Study each word and its meaning carefully.

Lacy could see the early morning sun peeking over the **horizon.**
> **horizon** — the line where the land and the sky seem to meet

The farm machine **plowed** the soil.
> **plowed** — used a tool to break up soil to prepare it for planting

The machine could also **harvest** when the plants were ripe and ready to be picked.
> **harvest** — to gather in a crop

Lacy's father was proud to have 10,000 **acres** of land.
> **acre** — unit used to measure land; one acre equals 43,560 square feet

Some farmers switched over to **hydroponics** when they lost their land.
> **hydroponics** — the science of growing plants without soil in water and chemicals

STARLIGHT, STARBRIGHT

by AL NUSSBAUM

Lacy left for the fields with her father shortly before dawn. When their huge tractor reached their work spot, a pink sun was peeking over the horizon. Their two fuzzy shadows stretched far over the flat ground. They were able to work without talking. Each knew what had to be done.

In fact, it was the machine the tractor pulled that did most of the work. The father had to drive the tractor at the proper speed and over the right ground. And Lacy had to make sure the machine was supplied with the seed, water, and special fertilizer it needed.

The machine did everything else. It plowed the rust-colored soil. It planted the seeds, and tested the ground so that just the right amount of fertilizer was added. Then it gave the seeds their first sprinkle of water and smoothed everything over.

Later, the machine would also harvest the crop and prepare it for long-term storage by canning or freezing. The machine had cost a fortune, but it was worth it.

Suddenly, the tractor lost power and stopped. Lacy knew her father's wrist alarm must have gone off. It had told him it was time to rest. Lacy climbed down from the machine and walked toward the tractor. Her father joined her on the ground just as her brother came racing up with their lunch. They sat together on the ground beside the tractor to eat.

"Craig," Lacy's father said. "It's a good thing we're not back in Illinois. The way you drive, you'd knock down all the trees in the state."

Craig smiled, "That's what you always say. No matter where we go, you and Mom always say it's a good thing we're not in

Illinois. But I don't think you mean it."

"I mean it, all right. This spot isn't perfect. The soil is too dry and the air is too thin, but it's ours. All ours. We have ten thousand acres of the best. By the time we die, we'll have built up a fine farm for Lacy and you. That's what my parents did for me and their parents did for them."

The father paused a moment, then continued. "If the cities hadn't kept getting bigger, using more and more farmland as they grew, we'd still be in Illinois. But we had to sell our land to make room for a city, and now this is the best place for us. We're right where we should be."

"You could have switched to hydroponics," Craig suggested. "That's what I would have done."

"That's not farming!" his father exploded. "Growing a crop in a tank of water and chemicals isn't natural."

"But," Craig insisted, "the people who do it are producing a lot with very little space."

"I would sooner have gone to New Detroit and slaved away my twenty-two hour work week for someone else—making monorails, or something."

"Do you mean that?"

"All you have to do is look around you. We're here. If I were not the kind of man who means what he says, we wouldn't be here."

Craig drove back to the house, leaving Lacy and their father in the field. There was still some work to do before they stopped for the day. But Lacy's father did

not get up to begin again. Instead, he stayed where he was, sitting on the ground with his back against the side of the tractor.

All at once, Lacy saw what the trouble was. Her father was staring at the star again. It was always the brightest spot in the sky except for the sun. It could be seen even when it appeared in the daylight.

"What do you think about when you look at that star?" Lacy asked.

"It's not a star. It's a planet," Lacy's father replied "I taught you that much."

"Well, you know what I mean. What do you think about?"

"I think about Illinois," her father said in a faraway voice. "I think about home and what it would be like to feel wind and rain on my face. It would be hard not to think about Earth when I'm watching it move across the sky."

"Why don't I feel that way?" Lacy asked.

"Maybe it's because you weren't born on Earth like Craig, your mom, and I. You were born here." Lacy's father smiled as though he had thought of something pleasant. "You're a Martian," he said. ◆

READING CHECK

Answer the following questions about "Starlight, Starbright." You may want to check your answers by reviewing details in the story.

1. When did Lacy and her father leave for work? What did they bring along to help them get the job done?

2. What kind of work were Lacy and her father doing?

3. Why did Lacy's parents have to sell their land in Illinois?

4. What choices did Lacy's father have after he sold his land? Why did he move to a new place and start a new farm?

5. Did Craig agree with his parents' decision to move to a new place? What would he have done instead?

6. What is the bright spot in the sky that Lacy's father stares at?

7. What are some of the things Lacy's father misses about life in Illinois? Why doesn't Lacy share his feelings?

WHAT DO YOU THINK?

1. How does Lacy's father feel about being a farmer? Do you think that Lacy and Craig will want to be farmers when they are old enough to choose their careers, or will they choose a different way of life?

2. This story has a surprise ending. The author does not tell you that the characters live on Mars until the very end. But there are clues that lead up to the surprise. What details suggest that this story takes place on another planet sometime in the future?

3. Imagine that you are looking at your own life 25 years from now. How do you think Earth will change in the future? In what ways do you think life will be as it is shown in "Starlight, Starbright?" In what ways will it be different?

VOCABULARY CHECK

Read the following sentences and choose the correct meaning of each word in **bold print.** Then write each word and its meaning on your paper.

1. At dawn, the sun was just a pink spot on the **horizon.**
   (point where a space ship lands, point where land and sky seem to meet)

2. Farmers are very busy when it is time to **harvest** the fields.
   (gather the crop, plan to buy land)

3. **Hydroponics** is a new way of providing food for people.
   (the science of careful cooking, the science of growing plants without soil)

4. Lacy's father dreamed of a farm of 10,000 **acres.**
   (unit of measure for land, workers that plant seeds)

5. Long before tractors and big machines were used, farmers **plowed** the soil by hand.
   (built barns and fences, prepared soil for planting)

STRATEGY CHECK

The paragraph below is based on the story "Starlight, Starbright." Choose the correct word to fill in each blank. Use the rest of the paragraph and what you remember about the story to help you. Then write the whole paragraph on your paper.

Lacy and her family lived and worked on a big f____. Her father believed that although this farm was not perfect, it was better to live there than in a large, crowded c____. Often Lacy's father stopped to stare at a bright spot in the sk____. When Lacy asked why he kept looking at that star, he reminded her it was a pl____. He looked at Earth up in the sky and r____his home back in Illinois.

◆ INTRODUCING ◆
"RANDY'S JOURNEY"

At first, Randy, a handsome golden puppy, seems at home with the Radcliffs. But Randy is not a dog that cares for staying home. He's a wanderer, in search of someone or something. Follow Randy's journey as he searches for his true homebase.

WORDS TO KNOW

The words in **bold print** are from "Randy's Journey." Study each word and its meaning carefully.

Randy was sometimes found wandering **aimlessly** along a road.
    aimlessly — without any aim, or purpose

He might stay in one place for a while, but a feeling of **wanderlust** would soon come over him.
    wanderlust — a strong desire to travel, or wander about

There was a trace of **aloofness** in Randy that kept him from getting too close to people.
    aloofness — coolness of manner

Some people gave Randy food and tried to **entice** him to stay.
    entice — tempt by offering some reward.

He wandered across the field to an **abandoned** apple orchard.
    abandoned — given up, deserted

For the first time in years, Katie was aware of a wonderful feeling of peace and **contentment.**
    contentment — satisfaction, happiness

RANDY'S JOURNEY

by SAM SAVITT

Jon Radcliff had always owned golden retrievers. When his old dog died, he bought another of the same breed. His new six-month-old puppy promised to be as handsome as any of the others.

The home the puppy was brought to was a magnificent white house on a high hill. It stood in the middle of rolling lawns and flower beds that were just beginning to come awake in the early spring sunshine.

Mr. Radcliff called the new arrival Randy, the same name he had given to all his other dogs. After the puppy was housebroken, he was allowed to run anywhere in the house. It was a large place with many carpeted rooms filled with armchairs and couches — the dream of any lively puppy.

It was an adult home that Randy had come to, and a rather cold one. Mrs. Radcliff didn't much care for dogs, and Mr. Radcliff was more interested in possessing them than loving them. Randy sensed this and avoided them both, but he got along well with everyone else. Annie, the cook, usually had a tasty tidbit for him, and the chauffeur always had a kind word. But the puppy had little real companionship. The only member of the household who played with him occasionally was Mr. Brenner, the old gardener, who also scolded whenever he found him digging in the flower beds.

By October, Randy had become a truly beautiful golden retriever. He had settled down quite a bit. Now that he was a year old, he wore a leather collar with his name engraved on the brass plate attached to it.

Randy was a loner. He sat on the front lawn a good part of the day, watching an occasional car or a horseback rider go by. He sometimes trotted down the long driveway to the road and stood gazing off

into the distance. But he never roamed away from the house.

He was a quiet, good-natured dog, seemingly happy and contented. His first winter with the Radcliffs was spent mostly indoors or down below the house, where he could gaze at the frozen pond and the neighborhood children skating on the far side.

But in early April, when the green began coming up through the brown fields, the golden-coated dog became restless. Soon he was spending more time in the surrounding countryside than on his front lawn. Often, when he did not show up for dinner, his owner sent the chauffeur to look for him. The man usually found him wandering aimlessly along a road. When the chauffeur called, Randy got into the car and rode home, sitting quietly in the backseat.

As spring became summer, Randy drifted farther away from the Radcliff house. Sometimes when he returned after being absent for a day or two, his owner locked him in the kennel for a while, hoping this might dampen his wanderlust. But the moment the dog was released, he was off again.

The countryside was spotted with farms and groups of small houses. Randy got to know the residents, and before long most of them became familiar with the handsome golden retriever. His warm, friendly manner charmed all who met him.

"Hi, Randy!" the children would cry as he came trotting up to them. He accepted their welcome with a great show of tail-wagging, grinning broadly as small hands reached out to him. He was never pushy. When he had had enough, he moved on up the road.

Randy stopped in occasionally to visit the Radcliffs, who had just about given up on him. Mr. Radcliff, however, was still hopeful that one day Randy would get over his roving ways and come back to stay.

But Randy was his own dog now. He made no attachments. He had become a drifter. Yet, anyone watching the purposeful way he trotted across the fields or up the

middle of a road might feel that here was a dog in search of something.

The Lucas farm lay in a small valley about two miles away from the Radcliff home. It was owned by Warren Lucas, who took great pride in his fine cows and kept the farm buildings neat and clean.

One morning in the middle of July, Randy stopped at the gate where the two Lucas children were playing in front of the low white farmhouse. Behind them, geese honked and ducks quacked in the barnyard. On the far hillside beyond, sheep grazed peacefully. In the meadows nearby, black-and-white spotted cows rested in the shade of the willow trees.

Perhaps the peacefulness of the scene held the dog there. For a moment, he seemed unable to make up his mind whether to go on or join the children. Then, suddenly, waving his golden tail in the air, he bounded up to the boy and girl. He seemed to be grinning from ear to ear, as if to say, Here I am. Aren't you lucky I've come to visit you!

The visit became a stay. The children fell in love with their new pet immediately. It certainly looked as if Randy had no intention of leaving. Warren Lucas checked with some of his neighbors about the dog's identity. They all remembered seeing him around, but the brass plate on his collar only said that his name was Randy, nothing else.

The Radcliffs' chauffeur spotted the golden retriever on the Lucas' front lawn a short time later. He recognized the dog and brought him home. Two days later, Randy was back with the Lucas family. The chauffeur picked him up again, and Randy returned to the Lucas home again.

This back-and-forth game went on through the month of August. At times, Randy returned to the Lucas farm every day. More often, two or three days went by before he made it back.

One evening in the beginning of September, Mr. Radcliff phoned Warren Lucas.

"Look here, sir," he announced. "My

chauffeur has picked up my dog at your place over 20 times this past month. That's getting a bit ridiculous, don't you think?"

"I'm sorry about that," the farmer replied, "but what can I do about it?"

"Not much, I suppose," Mr. Radcliff answered, "but I think that the best thing for me to do at this point is give him to you!"

Warren Lucas and his wife, Betty, were delighted to accept this beautiful gift, and, of course, the children were overjoyed. Randy was now officially theirs. For a while it seemed that the dog had found what he was looking for at last.

The Lucas dairy farm had everything that Randy loved — cows, pigs, sheep, chickens, geese, and flocks of doves. In the mornings, the dog joined his new owner in the cow shed while the milking machines were in action.

The young farmer became extremely fond of Randy. And, although the dog still romped with the children after school, he seemed to have become their father's companion. He followed the farmer about as he did his chores, and often rode beside him in the cab of the pickup truck. But Warren Lucas knew dogs, and he recognized in this one a certain independence that somehow kept them apart.

Randy stayed with the Lucas family through the winter. Then, one morning in early April, Randy walked out the driveway and turned east.

Warren Lucas saw him leave. He called

out, "Hey, Randy, come back!" But Randy was on his way.

That evening, the children asked where the dog had gone. Their father stood by the window, gazing in the direction Randy had taken. All that afternoon he had been watching, hoping against hope. He smiled sadly at the children.

"Randy has spring fever," he said. "He has the urge to travel on — maybe he'll come back."

But in his heart he knew that Randy never would.

All through the following summer, Randy drifted from one place to the next. He rarely went hungry, as most people were pleased to give him food when he came to the door. How could they resist the charming dog with the golden coat? Some tried to entice him to stay on, but he never did.

One afternoon in September, Randy was trotting north along the shoulder of a hardtop road. The day was very hot and humid for September. Randy was thirsty and, to add to his discomfort, police cars began appearing, driving slowly past him, going in both directions. Automobiles never bothered Randy. Right from the beginning of his travels, he had learned to keep out of their way. But these cars had speakers that blared loudly. Finally, ears tucked back, he turned off the road into the woods.

He followed an old cowpath downhill to a narrow strip of marshland. Here he lay in a shallow stream for a little while, lapping the water and feeling the wet coolness against his belly. Later, he got up, shook himself, and wandered across a brush-covered field to an abandoned apple orchard on the far side. Now he could no longer hear the loudspeakers. Up ahead, beyond the orchard, the woods became thick with tangled vines. Randy went around them and headed uphill to pick up the road once more.

A whimpering sound stopped him in his tracks. He stalked forward carefully to investigate and suddenly came face-to-face with a small boy. The child was standing alone in a mass of green ferns. His hair was plastered against his forehead, and his cheeks were stained with tears. His shirt was ripped by thorns and hung limply against his small body.

The boy had been lost in the woods since early that morning when he had wandered away from his home to pick berries.

The police loudspeakers had been calling him: "Billy, come to the road! Billy, come to the road!" But Billy could not hear them, and even if he had, he would not have known where the road was.

To Randy, the child was no different from the many other children he had met. Randy's wagging tail and grinning face told Billy this was a friend. A friend was what Billy needed now more than anything in the world. His little hands reached out to clutch the leather collar, and Randy started off in the direction he had been going. He was in no hurry, so he walked slowly to allow the boy to keep up. At one time, the child stumbled and let go. Randy stopped and waited for him to rise and take hold once more.

The pair emerged from the woods onto the road. A patrol car pulled up alongside them. A policeman got out and picked up the child. He held the back door open for Randy, who leaped in without a moment's hesitation.

They arrived in front of a small farmhouse a short time later. Billy's mother came rushing to the police car when she saw her son in the front seat beside the officer. She wept with joy when she held the child in her arms.

"Oh, you found him! You found him!" she cried over and over again.

The officer smiled. "It wasn't me that found your boy, ma'am," he declared. "It was this dog that did it!"

He pointed to Randy. "Saw them both come out of the woods together, the dog leading and the boy hanging on."

Of course, Randy became an instant hero. He did not know what great feat he had accomplished, but he was not one to question the praise he was suddenly receiving. He was invited into Billy Armor's home and given an enormous meal, the kind he had not had in a long time.

Randy lived with the Armors for more than two weeks. Mrs. Armor wanted to keep him, but felt it her duty to find out who owned this treasure. She made constant inquiries and ran an ad in the lost-and-found section of the newspaper, but there were no answers.

She groomed the dog every day until his coat took on an added shine. The family would have been delighted if Randy had chosen to live with them forever, but one cool afternoon in the beginning of October, Randy hit the trail once more.

Katie Conklin lived in a shabby brown house along one of the many dirt roads in the center of the county. She was a small woman, thin and slightly bent. There was a gray look about her — her shoes, and dress, and hair all seemed faded. But her eyes were dark and lively.

Katie had been born in this house. It had been a working farm then. The barn had been filled with horses and cows, and the summer fields had been green with corn. She had especially loved the time of haying and late August, when vegetables and fruits were stored for the winter. But after her husband died, the farm went downhill rapidly, for they had no children to carry on. Her only visitor was an elderly man who came up from the store to bring her food.

Day after day, she sat by her kitchen window and stared out at the changing seasons. Now it was early autumn. The days were still warm, but in the morning there was frost in the long valley below the house.

For the past week, Katie had been aware that a beautiful, golden-colored dog was in the area. Once she had seen the dog go by on the road, and just the day before she had noticed him moving alongside the fence behind the barn.

He made her think of a small brown dog she had when she was a child — it seemed so long ago. Way back in her memory, she could almost see him — leaping and barking with joy whenever they met.

The next morning Katie sat on her porch, hoping to see the golden dog again. He did not appear that day or the next, but on the afternoon of the third day, she saw him from her bedroom window — this time trotting up the road, heading in the direction of her house.

Katie quickly wrapped a shawl around her shoulders and hurried down the porch steps to the edge of the road.

As Randy came along, she stooped forward and reached out her hand. "Hey, big dog," she called softly.

Randy stopped just beyond her reach. In the past, he had only been approached like this by children. He seemed suspicious for a moment, but because he had such a friendly nature, he walked up to Katie and allowed her fingers to stroke the top of his head.

Katie's hand touched his collar. She turned her head to one side and squinted her eyes so that she could read the brass plate more easily. She rubbed its surface with her thumb to clear away the grime it had collected.

"My, you have a beautiful name," she said. "A long time ago," she said with a smile, "I had a dog like you—not as pretty perhaps, but he was a nice dog and I loved him very much."

Randy did not understand a word she was saying, but something held him there. He closed his eyes, panting softly, as Katie's gentle hand stroked his thick fur.

"How would you like to come in for a drink of water?" she asked.

She straightened up and turned back to her house.

Randy remained standing where he was. He seemed puzzled — and uncertain. Then he followed her up the porch steps and sat facing the door.

Katie went inside and quickly returned with a bowl of cool water. She placed it on the floor in front of him. The dog was not thirsty, but he took a few courteous laps.

Afterward he returned to the road and continued on his way. He looked back once to see Katie still on the porch, her pale face turned toward him.

Randy returned two days later. He approached Katie's house from the field behind it late in the day. The sun had already set, but a pink glow remained.

A faint yellow light appeared in one of the windows as Randy came up to the back porch and lay down. The evening was warm, and soon the air was alive with the sounds of the forest.

The door suddenly opened and Katie came out. She seated herself in a rocking chair, then saw Randy in the dark below her.

She was not startled. It was almost as if she expected him to be there.

"Good evening, Randy," she said quietly. "Why don't you come up and sit here beside me?"

She held out her hand and Randy came up to it, ducking his head slightly so that her fingers could reach the soft fur of his neck. They sat there together until the evening deepened into night and the stars glittered overhead.

Katie Conklin knew that she had given up. She had separated herself from the outside world and had allowed her loneliness to take over. Now, for the first time in years, she was conscious of a wonderful feeling of peace and contentment.

For a few moments, Katie fell asleep, but the chilly night air awakened her. The golden dog was no longer there. She peered into the darkness and called his name. Then she rose to her feet and walked slowly back into the house.

The following night, Randy came by again. It had turned cold, and this time Katie invited him to come in. But Randy preferred to stay on the porch. Katie spread out an old blanket for him to lie on, and in the morning she rose early to feed him a bowl of warm mush, which she had prepared the night before.

These visits went on into the middle of November. They became more and more frequent. Each time Randy went away, Katie eagerly looked forward to his return.

Before long he came into the house and slept beside her bed every night, stretched out on a large flowered pad she had made for him. She also bought herself a warm coat and new, comfortable shoes.

Soon they were walking together every day. Katie stepped more briskly now to keep up with her dog. Randy shortened his stride to help her.

When spring came, Katie put in a vegetable garden and planted flowers along the front of the house. Later that summer, she had the house painted white with green trim.

Randy never roamed again. Everyone had thought he was just a drifter who followed an endless trail. But Randy had been in search of something — someone who really needed him. When he found Katie Conklin, he was content to spend the rest of his life with her. ◆

READING CHECK

Answer the following questions about "Randy's Journey." You may want to check your answers by reviewing details in the story.

1. What did Randy do when he became restless in early April? What did his owner do to keep him home? What did Randy do then?

2. What was there about the Lucas farm that seemed to attract Randy when he saw it? What did Warren Lucas seem to notice about Randy later on?

3. How did Warren Lucas explain Randy's disappearance to his children?

4. Where did Randy find Billy? How did Billy know that Randy was friendly?

5. What did Mrs. Armor do to try to find Randy's owner? What was the result of her efforts?

6. How had Katie Conklin spent her days before Randy appeared? What did Randy remind Katie of?

7. At the end of the story, what things did Randy do for Katie that showed he felt at home with her?

WHAT DO YOU THINK?

1. How might living with a dog like Randy change Katie Conklin's life? How might living with Katie change Randy's wandering ways?

2. What do you think Randy might have been looking for on his long journey? Why do you think he kept leaving each place he stayed at?

3. If a dog like Randy appeared at your home, what would you do?

VOCABULARY CHECK

Read the following sentences and choose the correct meaning of each word in **bold print.** Then write each word and its meaning on your paper.

1. Many people were kind to Randy, but few could **entice** him to stay for long.
   (force, tempt)

2. One morning, Randy wandered **aimlessly** up the road to the Lucas farm.
   (on his own, without purpose)

3. Some people who saw Randy on the road may have thought he had been **abandoned.**
   (given up, left at home)

4. With Katie, Randy no longer seemed to have an **aloofness** about him.
   (hunger, coolness)

5. When the long journey ended, both Randy and Katie must have had a feeling of **contentment.**
   (excitement, satisfaction)

6. Randy's **wanderlust** may have been cured when he found a home.
   (desire to travel, need to make friends)

STRATEGY CHECK

The paragraph below is based on the story "Randy's Journey." Choose the correct word to fill in each blank. Use the rest of the paragraph and your knowledge of the story to help you. Then write the whole paragraph on your paper.

One morning, Randy stopped to watch the Lucas ch____ play on their farm. He seemed unable to make up his m____ whether to go or stay. He d____ to stay with the Lucas family. The Radcliffs' chauffeur spotted Randy outside and br____ him home. Two days later, Randy r____ to the Lucas farm. This went on every day until Mr. Radcliff decided that the best thing to do was to g____ Randy to the Lucases.

"POEMS ABOUT HOMEBASE"

The poems that you will read here bring to life very different kinds of homebases. "Children of the Desert" is part of a book-length poem filled with details that allow you to see and feel, to really experience life on the desert. "Sunset (St. Louis)" also creates a picture. Read carefully and discover the details and feelings that reveal the beauty to be found on ordinary city streets.

WORDS TO KNOW

The words in **bold print** are from "Poems About Homebase." Study each word and its meaning carefully.

A smoky **haze** filled the sky.
> **haze** — a fog-like mixture of dust and smoke in the air

The colors reflected in the water made it look as if the water was covered with a beautifully colored **mantle.**
> **mantle** — coat or cloak

The city had a large **levee** where many boats pulled in to dock.
> **levee** — a landing place on a river

The boats **moored** for the night looked as peaceful as if they were resting.
> **moored** — tied up

Twilight is a good time to watch the sky.
> **twilight** — the way the light in the sky looks just after sunset

The train rushed along the tracks as if it was **cleaving** a space for itself through the peaceful evening.
> **cleaving** — splitting apart, cutting through

CHILDREN OF THE DESERT

by BYRD BAYLOR

This is no place
for anyone
who wants
soft hills
and meadows
and everything
green
green
green . . .

This is for hawks
that like only
the loneliest canyons
and lizards
that run
in the hottest sand
and
coyotes
that choose
the rockiest trails.

It's for them.

And for
birds
that nest
in cactus
and sing out over
a thousand thorns
because
they're where
they want to be.

It's for them.

And for
hard skinny plants
that do without water
for months
at a time.

SUNSET
(St. Louis)

by SARA TEASDALE

Hushed in the smoky haze of summer sunset,
When I came home again from far-off places,
How many times I saw my western city
    Dream by her river.

Then for an hour the water wore a mantle
Of tawny gold and mauve and misted turquoise
Under the tall and darkened arches bearing
    Gray, high-flung bridges.

Against the sunset, water-towers and steeples
Flickered with fire up the slope to westward,
And old warehouses poured their purple shadows
    Across the levee.

High over them the black train swept with thunder,
Cleaving the city, leaving far beneath it
Wharf-boats moored beside the old side-wheelers
    Resting in twilight.

WHAT DO YOU THINK?

1. In Byrd Baylor's poem "Children of the Desert," she describes children who are not human. Who or what are the "children" described in this poem?

2. In "Children of the Desert," the poet describes a place that has "the loneliest canyons," "the hottest sands," and "the rockiest trails." Do you think the children of the desert find these things difficult or unpleasant? Explain why or why not.

3. In "Sunset (St. Louis)", Sara Teasdale wants to build very specific images. She uses color words and other words that appeal to your senses, especially your sense of sight, to help to get just the image she has of sunset in St. Louis. Describe three images from this poem that appeal to your sense of sight. Which of these images do you like or find easiest to understand? Why?

VOCABULARY CHECK

Read the following sentences and choose the correct meaning of each word in **bold print.** Then write each word and its meaning on your paper.

1. The boats were **moored** by sunset.
   (washed down, tied up)

2. On warm summer evenings, you can sometimes see a **haze** in the sky.
   (colorful rainbow, fog-like mixture of smoke and dust)

3. Sara Teasdale had fond memories of **twilight.**
   (train lights at nighttime, how the sky looks around sunset)

4. People gather at the **levee** to watch the boats pull in.
   (viewing tower, landing place)

5. The fast-moving train seemed to be **cleaving** the city.
   (clearing out of, cutting through)

6. The colors on the water made Sara Teasdale think of a person wearing a beautiful **mantle.**
   (colored ribbon, long cloak)

◆ UNIT REVIEW ◆

READING REVIEW

Homebase is about finding a home. Complete each sentence about a selection in the unit. Choose the best ending for each sentence. Then write the complete sentences on your paper.

1. In the beginning of "Claire's Cousin From Cairo," Lisa wanted to be friends with Claire because she thought ____.
   a. Claire was a good cousin
   b. Claire was moving overseas
   c. Claire's cousin was from Egypt
   d. Claire was good at lacrosse

2. In the story "Claire's Cousin From Cairo," Lisa discovered that her hometown ____.
   a. looked like Cairo, Egypt
   b. could be worthwhile
   c. had no lacrosse team
   d. was listed in an atlas

3. The article "The Butterfly Mystery" calls the monarchs' flight a "mystery" because no one knows ____.
   a. where they spend the winter
   b. how make their long flight
   c. what colors they are
   d. how long they live

4. In the story "Starlight, Starbright," Lacy has no happy memories of Earth because she had ____.
   a. worked on the farm
   b. left Illinois as a baby
   c. lived only on Mars
   d. been blinded by starlight

5. In the story "Randy's Journey," Randy saved Billy Armour's life by ____.
   a. bringing him food
   b. getting help
   c. leading him out of the woods
   d. carrying him home

6. At the end of "Randy's Journey," Randy found contentment in ____.
   a. the friendship of a lonely woman
   b. saving the life of a small boy
   c. traveling the highways
   d. visiting a farm family

VOCABULARY REVIEW

Review some words about homebases. Choose a word from the list to replace the words in **bold print** in each sentence below. Then write the new sentences on your paper.

explore	**roamed**	**drifter**
possessing	**migrate**	**exploded**

1. **A person who goes from place to place without a purpose** might travel forever and never find a homebase.

2. Many animals **travel from one area to another** every year.

3. Kate was more interested in having Randy as a companion than she was in **owning** him.

4. As Randy **wandered around** the countryside, he met many people who loved him.

5. It is possible to **travel and learn about new places** in an atlas or travel books.

6. Craig spoke calmly, but his father **spoke angrily** when he expressed his feelings about farming without land.

WRITING ABOUT HOMEBASE

1. In the story "Claire's Cousin from Cairo," Lisa is excited about the idea of meeting someone from another country, and has many questions to ask. If you were to meet a student who really does live in another country, what would you ask that person? List five questions you would want to ask.

2. Choose an animal that migrates a long distance every year: an insect, such as the monarch butterfly; a bird, such as the arctic tern; a fish, such as the salmon; or a mammal, such as the gray whale. Check encyclopedias and other reference books to learn the migrating habits of the animal you chose. Write one paragraph that describes the animal's route of migration. Write a second paragraph that describes any unusual features of the migration.

UNIT

·2·

A HELPING HAND

You try to do something, but, no matter how hard you try, you are not able to accomplish it on your own. It's time for some help. Sometimes a helping hand can give you that extra bit of effort you need, or give you an idea you hadn't thought of, or show you something you hadn't seen on your own.

In "The Third Jump" the great track and field star, Jesse Owens, tells about how he found help and friendship in the man who was supposed to be his enemy. In the story "The Secret Plan" a group of kids get together to try and solve a problem that no one else has been able to handle. The article "The Friends of Trees" is about people who make life in the city a little easier for trees, so that trees can make life a little easier for people. The two poems that end this unit, "Portrait" and "Direction," are about important people in your family who can help you understand the things that really matter.

Each of these selections is about how people help each other out. They show you that when you are stuck , the best way out of a problem is often to turn to another person. Two heads are often better than one.

UNDERSTANDING WORDS IN SENTENCES

Words About a Helping Hand. Certain words in this unit describe what it means to give a helping hand. Six of those words are in **bold print** in the sentences below. Use the rest of each sentence to help you choose the correct meaning of each word in **bold print**. Write the word and its meaning on your paper.

1. Luz Long **responded** to Jesse Owens' problem with some words of advice.
   (appeared, reacted)

2. Long was **confident** that his help would pay off.
   (certain, doubtful)

3. The four **companions** tried to come up with a plan to cut red tape in their city.
   (members of a team, those who spend time together)

4. At first, Michael felt satisfied that the club had **accomplished** its first good deed.
   (completed, prevented)

5. Members of the tree lovers' group act as **guardians** of the city's trees.
   (those who protect, those who plant)

6. Michael heard the **murmur** of his parents' voices.
   (harsh yell, soft sound)

◆ INTRODUCING ◆

"THE THIRD JUMP"

The Olympic Games of 1936 came at a time when the world was on the edge of a terrible war. In those games, Jesse Owens, a great athlete, faced an unusual challenge. Read this true story to find out who gave Jesse Owens the help he needed.

WORDS TO KNOW

The words in **bold print** are from "The Third Jump." Study each word and its meaning carefully.

At the time of the 1936 Olympics, Germany was a **dictatorship**, under Adolph Hitler.
   dictatorship — country ruled by one person with complete control of the government.

It was **ironic** that the Olympic games were being held in a country that would soon make war against other countries.
   ironic — the opposite of what might be expected

The athletes worked to save their energy for the broad jump and not use it all in the **preliminaries.**
   preliminaries — events coming before the main events, tryouts

Jesse Owens realized he had been **concentrating** too much on setting a record and not enough on his running style.
   concentrating — fixing attention

Jesse knew that Hitler expected him to give an **inferior** performance.
   inferior — of poor quality

Luz Long did not believe in the **supremacy** of one race over another.
   supremacy — being the best

A **unique** friendship formed between two men who could have been enemies.
   unique — like no other

THE THIRD JUMP

by JESSE OWENS and PAUL G. NEIMARK

Even though you weren't born until many years after, you've probably heard the story — the story of the 1936 Olympics and how I managed to come out with four gold medals. A lot of words have been written about those medals and about the one for the broad jump in particular. It was during that event that Hitler walked out on me and where, in anger, I supposedly fouled on my first two jumps against his prize athlete, Luz Long. The whole Olympics for me, and also for my country, seemed to rest on that third jump.

Yet what was written about me was only a half-truth without some other more important words. I want to say those words to you now.

Black athletes had gone to the Olympics before, and they had won before. But so much more was expected of me because this was the time of the greatest conflict between dictatorship and freedom the world had ever known. Adolf Hitler was arming his country against the entire world, and almost everyone sensed it. It was ironic that these last Olympic Games before World War II were scheduled for Berlin, where he would be the host. From the beginning, Hitler had made the games into a test between two forms of government.

The broad jump preliminaries came before the finals of the other three events I was in — the 100-meter and 200-meter dashes and the relay. How I did in the broad jump would determine how I did in the entire Olympics. For I held a world record in the broad jump that no one had ever approached before, except one man: Luz Long, Hitler's best athlete.

Long was a tall, sandy-haired, perfectly

built fellow. He had been known to jump over 26 feet in preparing for the games. No one knew for sure what he could really do because Hitler kept him under wraps. But stories were told that he had gone as far as I had, farther than anyone else in the world. I was used to hearing rumors like that, and tried not to think too much about it. Yet the first time I laid eyes on Long, I sensed that the stories hadn't been exaggerated. After he took his first jump, I knew they hadn't. This man was something. I'd have to set an Olympic record to beat him.

It would be tough. August in Berlin was muggier than May in Ann Arbor or Columbus. Yet the air was cool, and it was hard getting warmed up. The ground on the runway to the broad jump pit wasn't the same as that at home. Long was used to it. I wasn't.

His first jump broke the Olympic record—in the trials!

Did it worry me a little? More than a little. He was on his home ground and didn't seem to mind the pressure. In fact, he'd already done one thing I always tried to do in every jumping event and race I ran: discourage the competition by getting off to a better start.

Well, there was only one way to get back the psychological advantage. Right off the bat I'd have to make a better jump than he did. I didn't want to do it that way — it wasn't wise to use up your energy in preliminaries. Long could afford to make a

showing in the trials. This was his only event, the one he'd been groomed for under Hitler for years. I had to run three races, more than any other athlete on either team.

But I felt I had to make a showing right then. I measured off my steps from the takeoff board and got ready. Suddenly, an American newspaperman came up to me. "Is it true, Jesse?" he said.

"Is what true?" I answered.

"That Hitler walked out on you? That he wouldn't watch you jump?"

I looked over to where the German ruler had been sitting. No one was in his box. A minute ago he had been there. I could add two and two. Besides, he'd already snubbed me by refusing the Olympic Committee's request to have me sit in that box.

This was too much. I was mad, full of hate, and it made me feel wild. I was going to show him. He'd hear about this jump, even if he wouldn't see it!

I felt the energy surging into my legs and tingling in the muscles of my stomach as it never had before. I began my run, first almost in slow motion, then picking up speed, and finally faster and faster until I was moving almost as fast as I did during the 100-meter dash. Suddenly the takeoff board was in front of me. I hit it, went up, up high — so high I knew I was outdoing Long and every man who ever jumped.

But they didn't measure it. I heard the referee shout, "Foul!" in my ears before I even came down. I had run too fast, been concentrating too much on a record and not

enough on form. I'd gone half a foot over the takeoff board.

All the newspaper stories and books I've ever seen about that Olympic broad jump had me fouling on the next of my three tries, because the writers felt that made the story more dramatic. The truth is I didn't foul at all on my second jump.

I played it safe. Too safe. I was making absolutely sure I didn't foul. All right, I said to myself. Long had won his point. But who would remember the preliminaries tomorrow? It was the finals that counted. I had to make sure I got into those finals. I wasn't going to let Hitler anger me into throwing away what I'd worked ten years for.

So I ran slower, didn't try to get up as high during my jump. Look, I said to myself, if I can do 26 feet trying my best, I sure ought to be able to do a foot less without much effort. That would be enough to qualify for the finals, and there I'd have three fresh jumps again. That's where I'd take apart Luz Long.

It's funny how sometimes you can forget the most important things. I forgot that I wasn't the kind of guy who could ever go halfway at anything. More than that, no sprinter or jumper can really take just a little bit off the top. It's like taking a little bit off when you're working a mathematical problem or flying an airplane through a storm. You need the total concentration and total effort from beginning to end. One mistake and you're dead. More than that, my whole style was geared to giving everything I had, to using all my speed and energy every second of what I was doing.

So my second jump was no good.

I didn't foul. But I didn't go far enough to qualify, either. It wasn't just Long and Owens in the event anymore. There were dozens of other participants from other countries, and a bunch of them — too many — were now ahead of me.

I had one jump left.

It wasn't enough.

I looked around nervously, panic creeping into every cell of my body. On my right was Hitler's box. Empty. His way of saying I was a member of an inferior race who would give an inferior performance. In back of that box was a stadium containing more than 100,000 people, almost all Germans, all wanting to see me fail. On my right was the broad jump official. Was he fair? Yeah, but a Nazi. If it came to a close call, a hairline win-or-lose decision, deep

down didn't he, too, want to see me lose? Worst of all, a few feet away was Luz Long, laughing with a German friend of his, unconcerned, confident.

They were against me. Every one of them.

Did I find some hidden resource deep within me, rise to the occasion, and qualify for the finals — as every account of those Olympics says? No.

I found a hidden resource, but it wasn't inside of me. It was in the most unlikely place possible.

Time was growing short. One by one, the other jumpers had been called and taken their turns. What must have been 20 minutes or half an hour suddenly seemed like only seconds. I was going to be called next. I wasn't ready. I wanted to shout it —

I wasn't ready!

Then the panic was total. I had to walk in a little circle to keep my legs from shaking, hold my jaw closed tight to stop my teeth from chattering. I didn't know what to do. I was lost. If I gave it everything I had, I'd foul again. If I played it safe, I wouldn't go far enough to qualify. *And this is what it all comes down to,* I thought to myself. Ten years and 4,500 miles to make a fool of myself and not even reach the finals!

I couldn't even think anymore. I started to feel faint, began to gasp for breath. Instinctively, I turned away from everyone so they couldn't see me. But I couldn't help hearing them. The thousands of different noises of the stadium blended into one droning hum — ch-ch-ch-ch ch-ch-ch-ch, louder and louder in my ears. It was as though they were all chanting it. Hatefully, gleefully. Ch-ch-ch-ch. Ch-ch-ch-ch. CH-CH-CH-CH.

Suddenly I felt a firm hand on my arm. I turned and looked into the sky-blue eyes of my worst enemy.

"Hello, Jesse Owens," he said. "I am Luz Long."

I nodded. I couldn't speak.

"Look," he said. "There is no time to waste with manners. What has taken your goat?"

I had to smile a little in spite of myself — hearing his mixed-up American expression.

"Aww, nothing," I said. "You know how it is."

He was silent for a few seconds. "Yes," he said finally, "I know how it is. But I also know you are a better jumper than this. Now, what has taken your goat?"

I laughed out loud this time. But I couldn't tell him. I glanced over at the broad jump pit. I was about to be called.

Luz didn't waste words, even if he wasn't sure of which ones to use.

"Is it what Hitler did?" he asked.

I was thunderstruck that he'd say it. "I — " I started to answer. But I didn't know what to say.

"I see," he said "Look, we talk about that later. Now you must jump. And you must qualify."

"But how?" I shot back.

"I have thought," he said. "You are like I am. You must do it 100 percent. Correct?" I nodded. "Yet you must be sure not to foul." I nodded again, this time in frustration. And as I did, I heard the loudspeaker call my name.

Luz talked quickly. "Then you do both things, Jesse. You remeasure your steps. You take off six inches behind the foul board. You jump as hard as you can. But you need not fear to foul."

All at once the panic emptied out of me like a cloudburst.

Of course!

I jogged over to the runway. I measured my steps again. Then I put a towel parallel to the place half a foot before the takeoff board from where I wanted to jump.

I walked back to the starting spot. I began my run, hit the place beside the towel, shot up into the air like a bird, and qualified by more than a foot.

The next day I went into the finals of the broad jump and waged the fiercest competition of my life with Luz Long. He broke his own personal record and the Olympic record, too, and then I — thanks to him—flew from the ground to top that. Hours before, I had won the 100-meter and 200-meter dashes and helped our team to another gold medal and record in the relay.

During the evenings in the Olympic Village, I would sit with Luz and we would form an

even closer friendship. We were sometimes as different inside as we looked on the outside. But the things that were the *same* were much more important to us.

Luz had a wife and a young child, as I did. We talked about everything from athletics to art, but mostly we talked about the future. He didn't say it in so many words, but he seemed to know that war was coming and he would have to be in it. I didn't know then whether the United States would be involved, but I did realize that this earth was getting to be a dangerous place.

We talked, of course, about Hitler and what he was doing. Luz was torn between two feelings. He didn't believe in racial supremacy any more than he believed the moon was made of German cheese, and he was disturbed at the direction in which Hitler was going. Yet he loved his country and felt a loyalty to fight for it, if it came to that, if only for the sake of his wife and son. I couldn't understand how he could go along with Hitler under any circumstances, though, and I told him so.

He wasn't angry when I said it. He just held out his hands and nodded. He didn't explain because he didn't understand completely himself, just as I couldn't explain to him how the United States accepted its racial problems. So we sat talking about these things. We didn't come up with any final answers then, only with a unique friendship. For we were simply two uncertain young men in an uncertain world. One day we would learn the truth, but in the meantime, we would make some mistakes. Luz's mistake would cost him too much.

We made our only days together count. We crammed into them as much understanding and fun as we could. We didn't even stop when we got out on the track. Luz was at my side cheering me on for every event, except the broad jump, of course. There he tried to beat me for all he was worth, but nature had put just a little more spring into my body and I went a handful of inches farther.

After he failed in his last attempt to beat me, he leaped out of the pit and raced to my side — to congratulate me. Then he walked toward the stands, pulling me with him while Hitler was glaring, held up my hand, and shouted to the gigantic crowd, "Jesse Owens! Jesse Owens!"

The stadium picked it up. "Jesse Owens!" they responded — though it sounded more like *Jaz-eee-ooh-wenz!* Each time I went for a gold medal and a record in the next three days, the crowd would greet me with *Jaz-eee-ooh-wenz! Jaz-eee-ooh-wenz!*

Luz and I vowed to write each other after the games, and we did. For three years we wrote regularly, though the letters weren't always as happy as our talks at the Olympics had been. Times were hard for me and harder for Luz. He had had to go into the German Army, away from his wife and son. His letters began to bear strange postmarks. Each letter expressed more and more doubt about what he was doing. But he felt he had no other

choice. He was afraid for his family if he left the army. And how could they leave Germany?

The last letter I got from him was in 1939. "Things become more difficult," he said, "and I am afraid, Jesse. Not just the thought of dying. It is that I may die for the wrong thing. But whatever might become of me, I hope only that my wife and son will stay alive. I am asking you, my only friend outside of Germany, to visit them someday if you are able, to tell them about why I had to do this, and how the good times between us were. Luz."

I answered right away, but my letter came back. So did the next, and the one after. I tried to find out about Luz. No news. A war was on. Finally, when it was over, I was able to get in touch with Luz's wife and find out what had happened to him. He had been killed in Africa and was buried somewhere in the African desert.

Luz Long had been my competition in the Olympics. He was a white man — a Nazi white man — who fought to destroy my country.

I loved Luz Long, as much as my own brother. I still love Luz Long.

I went back to Berlin a few years ago and met his son, another fine young man. And I told Karl about his father. I told him that, though fate may have thrown us against one another, Luz rose above it. He rose so high that I was left with not only four gold medals I would never have had, but with the priceless knowledge that the only bond worth anything between human beings is their humanness. ◆

READING CHECK

Answer the following questions about "The Third Jump." You may want to check your answers by reviewing details in the story.

1. Where were the 1936 Olympics held? What was unusual about the location?

2. In which four events did Jesse Owens win gold medals? Which one did Jesse Owens consider the most important? Why?

3. What rumor did Jesse Owens hear about Luz Long right before his first trial jump? What advantages did Luz Long have over Jesse Owens in Berlin?

4. What happened on Owens' first and second trial jumps? Why did Owens feel panic before his third jump?

5. What advice did Luz Long give Jesse Owens before the third jump? What was the result of that jump? What were the results of the broad jump finals?

6. What were three things that Jesse Owens and Luz Long talked about as their friendship grew? How did Luz Long feel about his country?

7. How did Owens and Long stay in touch with one another after the Olympics? What happened to end their relationship?

WHAT DO YOU THINK

1. Why do you think Luz Long gave a helping hand to Jesse Owens in the Olympics? Do you think he took a risk in helping him? Explain.

2. Before Jesse Owens began the broad jump trials, he learned that Hitler had left the stadium. What effect could this have had on Owens' performance?

3. What do you think the meeting between Jesse Owens and Luz Long's son Karl must have been like? What questions might Karl Long have asked about his father?

VOCABULARY CHECK

Read the following sentences and choose the correct meaning of each word in **bold print.** Then write each word and its meaning on your paper.

1. Jesse Owens was determined not to give an **inferior** performance.
   (poor, exciting)

2. Hitler believed in the **supremacy** of one race over another.
   (being the best, being the fastest)

3. Jesse Owens fouled on his first trial jump because he was **concentrating** on breaking a record and not on the jump itself.
   (feeling strong, fixing attention)

4. The **preliminaries** determined who would take part in the finals.
   (tryouts, races)

5. It was **ironic** that Jesse Owens' victories were due partly to Luz Long.
   (fair, unexpected)

6. The friendship between the two atheletes was **unique** in many ways.
   (very close, like no other)

7. Germany had become a **dictatorship.**
   (country that fights another country, country controlled by one person)

STRATEGY CHECK

The paragraph below is based on the story "The Third Jump." Choose the correct word to fill in each blank. Use the rest of the paragraph and your knowledge of the story to help you. Then write the whole paragraph on your paper.

Jesse Owens had three ch___ to qualify for the broad jump event. On his first attempt, he jumped half a f___ over the takeoff board. On his second jump, he didn't f___, but he didn't go far enough to qualify. Before the third jump, he felt total p___. More than a hundred thousand p___ seemed to be waiting for him to fail. He then got a helping h___ from the one man he had thought of as his worst enemy.

65

◆ INTRODUCING ◆

"THE SECRET PLAN"

Michael and his friends think their new club should do something to help their city. But their first good deed may be one that gets them into trouble. Find out what happens when Michael and his friends decide to sneak out at night and start digging in a neighbor's yard.

WORDS TO KNOW

The words in **bold print** are from "The Secret Plan." Study each word and its meaning carefully.

Many accidents happened on the corner because of a large **hibiscus** bush.
   hibiscus — plant with large, colorful flowers

Michael and his friends nailed an old **tarpaulin** over the top of the frame to make a roof for the clubhouse.
   tarpaulin — a large sheet used to cover things

Linda Jean accused the boys in the clubhouse of **discriminating** against girls.
   discriminating — treating differently and unfairly

Michael thought **pruning shears** would make it easier to trim the bush.
   pruning shears — tool for cutting branches of trees and bushes

The boys were **petrified** when Mr. Hartwell came out of the house.
   petrified — frozen with fear

Michael's father was surprised that someone had thought of **eliminating** red tape in such an unusual way.
   eliminating — getting rid of

Could some **disgruntled** citizens have taken matters into their own hands when the city didn't act?
   disgruntled — annoyed

THE SECRET PLAN

by JOAN LOWERY NIXON

My father gets excited when he reads the newspaper at the breakfast table. Sometimes a story makes him mad, and he reads it out loud to my mother.

Sometimes my father reads a story to me, because he says a boy ought to be aware of what could happen if he fell in with bad companions.

At first I tried to tell him that Jimmy and Tommy Scardino and Leroy Parker weren't bad companions, but I found out it was just better to keep quiet and listen.

"Michael," he said one morning, "listen to this! The crime rate in Los Angeles is rising again! People being mugged, cars being stolen! A lot of it is being done by kids! Watch out, Michael!"

I nodded. What I had planned to do after school was work on the clubhouse we were building behind our garage, along with Tommy and Jimmy and Leroy. None of us wanted to steal cars. In the first place, it's a crime, and in the second place, we can't drive.

"Now will you listen to this, Dorothy!" my father suddenly exploded. "You know the Hartwells, who live on the corner —"

"I know them," I interrupted. "Mr. Hartwell is the meanest guy in the whole world. He yells at kids just because they cut across his lawn on their bicycles, and Linda Jean Hartwell is the ugliest, skinniest, most sickening girl in the whole —"

"I was talking to your mother," my father said sternly.

"Besides," my mother said, "don't make such dreadful faces at the table."

So I just reached for another piece of buttered toast and listened.

"It's all this red tape," my father said.

"What have the Hartwells got to do with red tape?" my mother asked.

"You know how hard it is to see around that corner, because of the huge hibiscus bush they've planted in front of their house? Well, heaven knows how many accidents have happened there because the driver's vision was blocked."

"Six," I said, but my father just scowled.

"But what about the red tape?" Mom asked, puzzled.

He punched at an item in the paper with his finger. "The city told him to trim his shrubbery, and he refused, so now they have to take him to court about it, and in the meantime more accidents could happen!"

"Oh, dear," my mother said. "It would be nice if the city could just come out and cut it down, wouldn't it?"

"Ha! That's what comes of getting involved in so much red tape!" My father started mumbling to himself and reading the rest of the newspaper.

I couldn't listen to any more because I had to leave for school. I had the bad luck to go out the front door just as Linda Jean Hartwell came by my house.

She smiled and said, "Hello, Michael Francis Cassidy," but I pretended I didn't see her.

She thought she was such a big shot because her dad owned a large auto repair shop over on Mariposa. I was going to ask her if she read in the newspaper about her father being in trouble with the city, but just then Leroy came by to walk to school with me, and I told him about it instead.

As soon as I got home from school, Mom told me to do my homework.

"Aw, Mom," I said, "I've just got a little bit, and I can do it tonight. All the guys are coming over to work on the clubhouse."

She looked discouraged, so I added, "You wouldn't want me to get weak and sickly because I didn't get any exercise, would you? I've been sitting in that school all day long, getting stiffer and stiffer."

Mom sighed. "All right, Michael. Play for an hour, and then you'd better come in and get busy with that homework if you know what's good for you!"

I ran right over to the clubhouse, taking along a bag of pretzels and some fruit juice. If we were going to work, we had to keep up our strength.

We had a lot of scrap lumber from the spot where they were building an apartment nearby, and we had made a pretty good frame. Then we nailed boards across the sides for walls, leaving some holes for windows to look out of in case an enemy was coming. Over the top we nailed an old tarpaulin. It was a pretty neat clubhouse.

The other guys showed up right away, and we got to work making a table for the inside. We figured there was plenty of room for all four of us to sleep there, as soon as it got warm enough, but we needed a table to hold all the food we'd have to take in with us.

We had just got inside our clubhouse and padlocked the front — well, the only door, when the whole thing was ruined by old Linda Jean sticking her head in the side window and asking what we were doing.

"This is a club just for boys!" I yelled at her. "Go away!"

"Why does it have to be just for boys? I want to join, too."

"Because that's the rules!" Leroy said.

Linda Jean got mad. "You're discriminating against me!"

Leroy turned to look at me, a worried expression on his face. "Oh-oh! We don't want to discriminate. My pop says discrimination is the curse of the world."

"It is, if it's about black people, like you," I explained. "But it's perfectly legal to keep girls out of our club."

His face brightened. "Are you sure?"

"I'm positive," I said. "There aren't any girls in the YMCA, are there?"

"That's right," Jimmy and Tommy said together.

Jimmy and Tommy are just ten months apart and in the same grade, and sometimes they act like a couple of twins.

"Okay, then," Leroy said to Linda Jean. "We just voted you out!"

Linda Jean made a face at us. "All right for you! I'm going to shadow you! I'll be a spy and watch everything you do!"

We all tried to get out the door at once to catch her, but that was a big mistake, because Tommy and Leroy got stuck in the doorway, and three boards fell off, along with the padlock. By the time we got the doorway nailed back together again, she had disappeared.

She wasn't kidding, though, when she said she was going to spy on us. Later, she kept popping out from behind the garage every few minutes. We pretended we didn't see her, so she chucked a few dirt clods on the roof of the clubhouse.

While we were figuring what we'd have to do to get rid of her, we could hear her mother call her, three houses away.

"Linda Jean!" her mother yelled, "Come home and practice the piano!"

Linda Jean had to go home, and pretty soon we could hear that poor old piano thumping.

"As long as the piano is going, we're safe," Jimmy said.

"That girl is going to grow up to be as mean as her old man," Tommy said.

That reminded me of the story in the newspaper, so I told Tommy and Jimmy about it.

"My dad said it would take months for the city to get anything done about that hibiscus bush," I said.

"I think somebody ought to help the city out," Leroy said. "Somebody could sneak out there at night and trim the bush, and nobody'd be the wiser."

"Yeah!" Tommy said. "And it would save the city a lot of trouble. Can't you just picture Linda Jean's face when she looked out her window and the bush was cut back?"

We all laughed like crazy, until finally I guess the idea hit all of us at the same time.

"Every club ought to have some kind of purpose," I said.

"And our purpose could be to do good deeds," Tommy added.

"This could be a real good deed — even save lives if there weren't any more accidents at that corner," I said.

"Maybe we'd get a medal from the city," Jimmy suggested.

"Unh-unh," Leroy told him. "If we're going to do *that* kind of good, then we'd better keep quiet about it, or it'll spoil everything."

"That's what I think, too," I said. "So, let's meet tonight, after everybody is asleep, and take care of that bush!"

I began to feel a little shiver up my backbone after I had spoken the words, and I could tell that the others felt the same way.

"You think we can get away with it?" Jimmy whispered.

"Sure," I said. "If we meet at 11 o'clock, our parents will all be asleep, and I'll bring my dad's pruning shears."

Everyone was silent for a moment. Finally Leroy spoke up. "I'm coming."

"Me, too," Tommy said.

Jimmy nodded. "Count me in." His eyes were wide. "What happens if we get caught?"

"We won't get caught," I said, trying to sound confident. I had wondered the same

thing myself. There was no telling what might happen to us.

I had a hard time staying awake, and I kept wondering what the other guys were doing. Mom came in and looked at me and patted the covers around my shoulders, even though I had pulled them up to my ears so she wouldn't notice I still had my clothes on.

Finally their door shut, and in a little while everything was quiet.

I turned on my flashlight and looked at my watch. It was about 10:30. So far, everything was going all right. I quietly put my sneakers on and walked carefully out into the hall, moving one cautious step at a time. It was kind of hard to see in the dark.

At the bend in the hallway, I bumped smack into my father. He let out a yell, and so did I. Quick as anything, he grabbed my shoulder and flipped on the light switch. He had what was left of a glass of water in his hand. Most of it was dripping down his pajamas.

My mother came running down the hall, crying, "Is it a burglar? Is it a burglar?"

She was waving a wooden coat hanger in one hand, and I guess I was glad enough I wasn't a burglar when I thought about how it would feel to be jumped on by my father, with my mother whacking away with a coat hanger.

They both looked surprised to see me. "Why, it's Michael!" Mom said. "What's going on? Why are you dressed?"

They were both staring at me, and I thought I had to say something, so I mumbled, "Isn't it morning yet?"

My mother chuckled and put her arms

around me. "You poor thing," she laughed. "You just dreamed that it was morning."

"Is that what I did?"

"Yes, dear." She patted my shoulder. "Now, you just take off your clothes and put on your pajamas again and have a good night's sleep."

I went back into my bedroom and shut the door. I could hear the murmur of my parents' voices for a long time, and I kept turning on my flashlight and looking at my watch. It got closer and closer to 11:00. If I didn't show up, the others would think I was scared, and they'd all go home.

Pretty soon it was two minutes to 11:00. I opened the door carefully, so it wouldn't squeak, and listened.

Back in my parents' bedroom I could hear my father snoring, which meant if I were quiet enough, I could make it out the back door.

I felt my way along the dark hallway, inch by inch.

Finally, I made it to the kitchen and slowly opened the back door without a sound. I gave a big sigh of relief.

Leroy was already in the clubhouse when I got there. "Am I glad to see you!" he said. "It's spooky in here when it's dark."

"Do you think the others are coming?" I asked.

"What'll we do if they don't show?"

I shrugged. "We can do it ourselves."

But just then, Tommy and Jimmy crawled in the doorway. Jimmy was rubbing his eyes.

"He fell asleep," Tommy said. "I had a terrible time waking him up without waking the whole house. He kept mumbling, 'Go

away,' so I finally put my hand over his mouth to keep him quiet, and he bit my finger."

"You can't blame people for things they do when they're asleep," Jimmy complained.

I had put the pruning shears in the clubhouse, and I felt around in the dark until I found them. "I've got the pruning shears right here."

Tommy felt them. "Are those ours? My dad's been griping at me, 'cause he can't find ours, and he thinks I had something to do with their being missing."

"No," I said, "they're ours. My dad puts his name on every tool he owns."

"I know why, too," Leroy said. "Because when you left his hoe and rake over on the sidewalk and —"

"Never mind," I said. "If we're just going to sit around and tell dumb stories, we'll never get this job finished."

"Okay," Leroy said. "We're all set to go."

Single-file, we crept through the yard and down the driveway and three houses away to the Hartwells' front yard. I hadn't taken a good look at the bush, and close to it, it looked sprawled out and big.

"No wonder this thing causes accidents," Jimmy said.

I decided how far down we should prune, and got busy. The shears sounded awfully loud in the darkness, and we all looked around nervously.

We waited, but nothing happened, so I tried it again. The branches were thin and easy to cut, and it didn't take long until I was finished, I stepped back to admire the job.

"That's still too high," Leroy said. "You didn't take enough off."

The others nodded agreement, so Leroy took the pruning shears from me and set to work.

When he finished, the bush looked awful. It was ragged and shorter on one side than the other, so Tommy took the shears and tried it.

Jimmy kept objecting to the way Tommy was pruning the bush, so finally he had a turn. When he finished, that great big old hibiscus bush was only about two feet tall.

"We made a mistake," Tommy said.

"I'll say we did!" I answered.

"I mean, we shouldn't have just pruned it. First thing you know, the whole bush will grow back, and it will be as bad as it was before."

"You're right," Leroy said. "We should dig it up."

I examined what was left of the bush. I remembered how pretty it was when it was blooming. "If we just dug it up, that would be stealing," I said.

We all thought about that a minute. Then I had a great idea. "But how about if we dug it up and planted it some place else in their yard?"

"Good enough!" Leroy said.

I sent Jimmy back to my house to get the shovel so we could dig, and in a few minutes he was back with it.

We all had to take turns digging, because that hibiscus had put down some big roots, but finally we got the thing loose.

"Now where do we put it?" Jimmy asked.

Tommy had been scouting around. "There's an empty space in an old flower bed next to their back porch. That would be a perfect place."

It was a good place, and the ground was soft enough so that it wasn't too hard to dig a hole.

We got the bush in and tamped down the dirt around it and were ready to congratulate ourselves for doing a good civic-minded job when Leroy blew the whole thing.

He dropped the shovel on the driveway, and it made a terrible clatter. A light flipped on in the Hartwell house.

We all froze.

We heard Mr. Hartwell yell, "Who's out there?" Before we could even think, he came rushing out on his porch, waving what looked like a gun.

"I see you!" he yelled.

I knew he really couldn't see us because it was too dark, but the thought of a gun had me petrified.

"Stop!" he yelled, and he came charging toward us, right off that porch. When he fell into the hibiscus bush, he made a terrible noise.

Mrs. Hartwell was inside the house yelling, "Call the police!" And dumb old Linda Jean was calling, "Mama! Mama! Help!"

I grabbed the shovel, and Tommy, Jimmy, Leroy, and I ran away from that place so fast we could have broken the school track record.

"Scatter!" I yelled, and we did — each of us going to his own home.

I dropped the shovel on the grass in back and let myself into the kitchen door, my hands shaking so hard I didn't know how I'd get the door open. Somehow I managed to go quietly to my room without waking anyone, because I could still hear my father snoring.

I was too nervous to get undressed. I just took off my shoes and climbed under the blanket. I could hear a police siren coming down Santa Monica, and it stopped in front of the Hartwells'.

My father woke up and said, "Did you hear something?" But my mother just murmured at him, and they both went back to sleep.

I began to relax. The more I thought about it, the better I felt. We had cut through some red tape and accomplished what the city couldn't do without going to court. And Mr.

Hartwell would get used to that bush being by his back steps and stop falling into it after a while. They'd never know who to thank.

I closed my eyes and got ready to go to sleep.

Then suddenly a thought hit me so hard I sat upright in bed, breaking into a cold sweat.

The police *would* know who was responsible, and they'll tell Mr. Hartwell, and maybe he'd come after me. *I had left the pruning shears, with my father's name on them, right there in plain sight!*

The next morning, the story was in the newspaper. My father got excited when he read it, and my mother did, too.

"Right in our own neighborhood!" she cried. "To think, only three doors away!"

My father kept reading the item, "Hartwell told reporters he thought that four large men in a white truck did it. He seemed angry that his wife had phoned the police."

"Four men in a white truck?" I sputtered without thinking. "But that's impossible!"

"I just don't understand what kind of a crime it was," Mom said. "It doesn't seem logical that someone would chop up his hibiscus bush and then replant it next to his back porch. What's the purpose?"

My father frowned. "It is strange, isn't it?"

"Maybe it was somebody trying to save the city some red tape," I said.

My father stared at me for a moment, and suddenly his face lit up. "Why, I never thought of that! Somebody who read the item yesterday and thought of eliminating some red tape! Very extraordinary!"

One thing was worrying me. "Does the article say they found any clues?"

"Now that's a point worth checking," Dad said. "Suppose they track down all the people who've had heaven knows how many accidents on that corner —"

"Six," I interrupted.

"And see what they were doing last night. Sounds like a highly disgruntled taxpayer."

"But was anything left behind. . . any . . . uh . . . tools?" I persisted.

"That's a point, all right," Dad said.

"Listen to me, Dad. Did anybody leave anything behind?"

My father turned to look at me. "Anything like what?"

"Well . . . uh . . ." I didn't know just how to put it. "Any . . . uh . . . things like tools with somebody's name on them?"

He snorted. "Now what kind of fool would commit a crime and leave a tool with his name on it?"

He went on talking to Mom, so I supposed the newspaper article didn't mention it. What I couldn't figure out was, if the police had found the pruning shears with our name on them, why hadn't they come to arrest me last night? It didn't make sense.

I left for school early. There was just one slim chance that the shears hadn't been discovered. It could accidentally have been hidden under the pile of hibiscus branches.

I started poking around the branches, but Mr. Hartwell came out on his front porch and yelled, "Hey, you snoopy kid! Get out of there!"

He had a couple of bandages on his arms and chin, so I guess it probably wasn't much fun falling in what was left of the hibiscus bush.

I didn't answer him, just walked on toward school. I had seen enough to know that the pruning shears weren't there. The question was, where were they?

Leroy, Tommy, and Jimmy were there early, too, and we got together in a corner of the schoolyard. I told them about the missing shears.

"Neither of us took it," Tommy said. "We just beat it out of there. I've never been so scared in my life."

"I didn't take it." Leroy said.

"Okay," I said. "So what happened to it? If the police got it, we'd be arrested by now. It didn't just fly away."

"Cool it," Leroy whispered. "Here comes Linda Jean."

We all stood there, trying not to see her, staring at the school wall until she walked up and stopped.

"Hi," she said. "Are you talking about what happened at my house last night?"

"Uh . . . we were talking about all sorts of things," I said.

"Do you know my father thinks there were four men, and they drove away in a white truck?"

"That was in the newspaper."

"It was exciting," she said. "My father got real mad at my mother, because she called the police, and that was exciting, too."

"We heard the siren," Tommy said, but Jimmy nudged him, and he kept quiet.

"Were you talking about your club?" Linda Jean asked.

"Naw," I said.

"I want to join your club," she said.

"Look," I told her, "we already let you know that girls can't join our club!"

"Discrimination!" she sniffed.

That word kept getting to Leroy. Right away his face got troubled and he said, "Say, Mike, we don't want to get mixed up in any discrimination — even if it is just with girls."

"Leroy has the the right idea," Linda Jean said.

"Leroy, I keep telling you that not letting girls in a club is not really discrimination," I said.

Linda Jean rubbed the toe of her shoe back and forth on the ground. "I could probably take it to the Supreme Court, but I won't," she said. "It doesn't make any difference if you do want to discriminate against me, because things are different now."

Tommy groaned. "You mean the Supreme Court has made rulings about boys' clubhouses?"

"I mean that now I've got the price of admission," she said.

We all started to laugh and holler. That was really funny! Price of admission! What did she think our clubhouse was — a movie theater? That was the funniest thing we'd ever heard!

"My price of admission is a pair of pruning shears," she said.

We stopped laughing.

Jimmy looked at me. "What do we do, Mike?"

"Linda Jean Hartwell, you know that's blackmail!" I sputtered.

"No, it isn't," she said. "Not when people are discriminating against you."

Leroy frowned.

"You might even thank me for saving you," she added.

"How did you find the shears, anyway?" Jimmy asked.

"Well," she said, "while my mother ran to help my father, I went down to the corner to look for the police. I ran right into the shears."

I sighed. "I don't think we have much choice. We'll have to let her into the club."

Everyone groaned except Linda Jean, who had the same kind of evil grin on her face as the mad scientist in the late movie I wasn't supposed to watch last week.

"Tell me why you cut down my father's hibiscus bush," she demanded, but the bell rang, and I muttered, "We'll tell you everything at the clubhouse after school today."

After school, Linda Jean brought the shears to the clubhouse and also brought along some awfully good peanut butter cookies. I have to admit her mother is a good cook. I told Linda Jean about the red tape. She thought what we did was a good idea.

"My mother likes the bush better by the back door," she said. "She never liked it where it was in the first place. And when the city told us it blocked the view, she wanted my father to move it immediately."

"Then why didn't he?" Tommy asked.

"My father is very stubborn," she said. "And

a funny thing . . . he's been awfully nervous since that happened. I think that's why he was so mad at my mother when she called the police. He couldn't wait to get rid of them."

"Well," I said, "I think we had better get some new ideas about what to do in our club. This helping the city in the middle of the night is too dangerous."

The boys nodded, but Linda Jean looked surprised. "I don't think it's that dangerous. Think of all the good we can do."

Tommy stuffed another peanut butter cookie in his mouth. "I don't think I want to do good anymore," he said.

Linda Jean got mad. "You're acting like a bunch of sissies! Just think of all the helpful things we can do. We'll be heroes! We'll save lives. Someday we might all be famous!"

I was going to say something mean when she said we were sissies, but I started thinking about the hero part and being famous and saving lives, and I kind of liked that.

"We could be called the Red Tape Gang, and strike for justice after dark!" she added.

"But what kind of things will we do?" Tommy asked.

"Who thought of digging up my father's bush?"

"Mike did," Jimmy said. "His father keeps reading in the newspaper about things that are going on and telling the whole family about them."

"That's perfect!" Linda Jean said. "Mike, you can be in charge of finding out what needs to be done around here."

"Big deal," I muttered.

"What we need is organization," she said. "Jimmy can be our scout, and Tommy can —"

I interrupted. "Linda Jean, we said you could be in our club, but you can't run things."

"I've got the shears," she said.

I looked her right in the eyes. "If you run things, I'd just as soon be in jail."

We stared at each other for a moment, then she shrugged and gave a little smile. "Okay. I don't care, anyway."

"I'm in charge," I said. "We can all look out for what needs to be done."

"I hope we don't find anything," Tommy grumbled, and Linda Jean scowled at him.

"I'd really like to be a scout," Jimmy said.

I sighed. "You can be a scout, then."

Jimmy and Linda Jean grinned at each other. I wondered if he remembered she was practically the enemy.

When the meeting broke up, we planned to get together any time there was an emergency. The signal would be to go outside and howl like a coyote. If we did it good and loud, everybody could hear it.

We were all a little scared in spite of Linda Jean's excitement, but we were determined not to back out now. There was no telling what might happen the next time we tried to eliminate red tape. ◆

READING CHECK

Answer the following questions about "The Secret Plan." You may want to check your answers by reviewing details in the story.

1. Why did many accidents happen at the corner where the Hartwells lived? Why wasn't the city able to do anything?

2. Why wasn't Linda Jean Hartwell allowed to join the club that Michael and his friends started? What did she say she would do then?

3. What idea did the boys come up with as a purpose for their club? What did they plan as their first act?

4. Why did the boys have trouble trimming the bush? Why did they decide to dig it up and move it?

5. What sound woke the Hartwells? What did the boys do then?

6. What had Michael left behind at the Hartwells? Why was he so worried about it?

7. Why did Linda Jean believe she had "the price of admission" to the clubhouse? How did Linda Jean explain the fact that the bush in her yard had not been moved earlier?

WHAT DO YOU THINK?

1. Do you think that private citizens should take action when a town or city does not move fast enough to correct a problem? Why, or why not?

2. What kinds of "good deeds" would you suggest for a club like the one organized by Michael and his friends?

3. Do you think that some clubs should be only for boys, or only for girls? Explain.

VOCABULARY CHECK

Read the following sentences and choose the correct meaning of each word in **bold print.** Then write each word and its meaning on your paper.

1. Linda Jean accused the club of **discriminating** against her.
    (lucking out, treating differently and unfairly)

2. The boys stood **petrified** for a moment after Leroy dropped the shovel.
    (frozen with fear, lost in thought)

3. Linda Jean said that her father was too stubborn to cut down the **hibiscus**.
    (plant with large flowers, plant that doesn't need water)

4. The **tarpaulin** on top of the clubhouse kept the inside dry.
    (metal roof, cloth cover)

5. Michael had the idea of **eliminating** red tape by trimming the bush.
    (getting rid of, trying to grow)

6. The **pruning shears** were evidence that Michael had been in the yard.
    (tool for planting seeds, tool for cutting branches)

7. Mr. Hartwell could have been **disgruntled** when the bush was moved, but he didn't seem to mind after all.
    (annoyed, puzzled)

STRATEGY CHECK

The paragraph below is based on the story "The Secret Plan." Choose the correct word to fill in each blank. Use the rest of the paragraph and your knowledge of the story to help you. Then write the whole paragraph on your paper.

    The boys approached the Hartwells' house late at n____. They found that the bush in the Hartwells' y____ was harder to trim than they had expected. They decided to dig it up and pl____ it near the house. Just as they finished, Mr. Hartwell w____ up and came charging toward them. Michael ran home and cl____ into bed. Suddenly, he r____ what he had left behind, in plain sight.

"THE FRIENDS OF TREES"

What can trees do for people in a big city? What can people do for the trees? Why do some people cut branches off of healthy trees? You'll find the answers in the article.

WORDS TO KNOW

The words in **bold print** are from "The Friends of Trees." Study each word and its meaning carefully.

Marianne Holden could not **restrain** herself when she saw a tree that needed pruning.
　　restrain — hold back

Tree lovers can take a course and earn a pruning **certificate.**
　　certificate — document stating that training has been completed

Members of the group learn how to **cultivate** the soil around the trees.
　　cultivate — prepare for growing

One benefit of trees is that they produce **oxygen** that people need to breath.
　　oxygen — a gas that is an important part of air

Trees can also **filter** the air, making it cleaner.
　　filter — strain out dirt or other unwanted parts

THE FRIENDS OF TREES

by WILLIAM E. GEIST

Marianne Holden could not restrain herself any longer. She whipped out her trusty 12-inch folding saw and attacked a Japanese pagoda tree.

"It feels sooo good," she said, standing on her tiptoes while she removed a limb the tree did not need. A wise guy walking by yelled "Timberrrr!" when the little branch dropped to the ground.

Marianne Holden is one of a group of more than 1,000 tree lovers who take care of New York City's trees. Members of the group take a course that leads to a pruning certificate. They not only prune trees. They also cultivate the soil around them, water and feed them, and serve as their guardians against dog walkers, and people who chain their bikes to the trees or nail messages on them.

There are about 600,000 trees planted on the sidewalks of New York. Street trees do not have the best growing conditions. Their soil is likely to contain a mixture of cement dust, salt, broken concrete, smashed glass, and rubbish that people toss away. And there is even very little of this poor soil; just under the sidewalk, there are sewers, drains, gas pipes, telephone cables, and the subways. Even the street lights keep the trees up all night.

For these reasons, city trees do not live as long as country trees. They live an average of seven years, rather than the 50 years or more they might live in the country.

Members of the tree lovers' group have spread the word about the benefits of trees in the city. Trees produce oxygen, filter the air, reduce noise, and they improve the value of the land. Still, some city residents

do not want trees. They even go so far as to cut them down. A passerby watching Marianne Holden prune a tree said he saw no real reason to have trees around that do not have "bananas or something" on them.

The city's Parks Department reports that 100,000 trees need pruning each year. Its workers prune about 40,000 a year, and the tree lovers' group helps to fill the gap.

Pruning trees in a big city can be an adventure. People are often suspicious about what the pruners are doing. Crowds will sometimes gather around and argue about which limb should be cut.

Marianne Holden believes that a pruner should be "an artist, not an executioner." Some people who like to prune, but don't know how, may get carried away.

One man climbed a tree in front of his apartment building to clip a dead limb. He cut his hand, fell out of the tree, and landed on a passerby who thought he was being attacked. The passerby slugged the pruner. Then the pruner staggered into the street and was bitten by a neighborhood dog.

After hearing this story, some people may decide that pruning trees in cities is just too dangerous. ◆

READING CHECK

Answer the following questions about "The Friends of Trees." You may want to check your answers by reviewing details in the article.

1. How do tree lovers in New York earn the right to prune trees?

2. What are some things people do to take care of the city trees? What do they protect them against?

3. What are two special problems that city trees have?

4. How long do city trees usually live compared to country trees?

5. What are three benefits that city trees provide?

6. What is one problem with pruning trees in crowded cities?

WHAT DO YOU THINK?

1. Do you think it is important that a big city have trees? Explain.

2. What did Marianne Holden mean by saying that a tree pruner should be "an artist, not an executioner?"

3. What is your favorite kind of tree? Why?

VOCABULARY CHECK

Read the following sentences and choose the correct meaning of each word in **bold print.** Then write each word and its meaning on your paper.

1. Someone who earns a pruning **certificate** should be qualified to prune a tree.
   (award, document)

2. A tree will grow better if someone takes the time to **cultivate** the soil around it.
   (prepare for growing, cover with bricks)

3. The tree lovers hope to **restrain** dog walkers and bike riders from harming the trees.
   (release, hold back)

4. Growing trees is an inexpensive way to **filter** the air.
   (strain out dirt, change the temperature)

5. Without **oxygen** from trees, the air would not be fit to breathe.
   (a gas, a flower)

STRATEGY CHECK

The paragraph below is based on the article "The Friends of Trees." Choose the correct word to fill in each blank. Use the rest of the paragraph and your knowledge of the article to help you. Then write the whole paragraph on your paper.

A group of about 1,000 people enjoys protecting city tr____. When a tree has too many br____, the tree lovers prune them. They g____ the trees against dog walkers. They w____ the trees and feed them. City trees do not l____ as long as country trees. One reason is the poor s____ they grow in.

"POEMS ABOUT A HELPING HAND"

Sometimes a helping hand means helping someone deal with a specific problem. This kind of help is very important, but what can be more important is the help you get in deciding on what will be important to you when you face many different kinds of problems. Read "Portrait," and "Direction" to discover examples of the love and support from family members that are a special kind of helping hand.

WORDS TO KNOW

The words in **bold print** are from "Poems About A Helping Hand." Study each word and its meaning carefully.

A person who has **wisdom** is able to make intelligent decisions
    wisdom — great knowledge or learning

Sometimes **craftiness** is a good quality to have in tricky situations.
    craftiness — cleverness, or slyness

PORTRAIT

by LOUISE GLUCK

A child draws the outline of a body.
She draws what she can, but it is white all through,
she cannot fill in what she knows is there.
Within the unsupported line, she knows
that life is missing; she has cut
one background from another. Like a child,
she turns to her mother.

And you draw the heart
against the emptiness she has created.

DIRECTION

by ALONZO LOPEZ

I was directed by my grandfather
To the East,
   so I might have the power of the bear;
To the South,
   so I might have the courage of the eagle;
To the West,
   so I might have the wisdom of the owl;
To the North,
   so I might have the craftiness of the fox;
To the Earth,
   so I might receive her fruit;
To the Sky,
   so I might lead a life of innocence.

WHAT DO YOU THINK?

1. The heart is often used as a symbol for love. Is the heart used as a symbol for love in the poem "Portrait?" Explain why or why not. Can the heart stand for anything else other than love in this poem? Explain what else the heart might stand for. Use lines from the poem to support your answer.

2. Alonzo Lopez says that he was directed by his grandfather to learn about power, courage, wisdom, and craftiness, and to appreciate the gifts of the earth and sky. Which of these qualities do you think is the most important? Explain.

3. If you were to write your own poem about receiving a helping hand from a person close to you, whom would you write about? What was the lesson or the helping hand that this person gave you?

VOCABULARY CHECK

Read the following sentences and choose the correct meaning of each word in **bold print.** Then write each word and its meaning on your paper.

1. Because of his **craftiness,** the grandfather was able to talk his way out of danger again and again.
   (beautiful voice, cleverness)

2. People describe the owl as a symbol of **wisdom.**
   (knowledge, magical power)

READING REVIEW

Each selection in this unit describes a certain kind of assistance — a helping hand at the right time. Complete each sentence about a selection in the unit. Choose the best ending for each sentence. Then write the completed sentences on your paper.

1. In the story "The Third Jump," before Jesse Owens could compete for a medal in the broad jump, he had to ___.
   a. beat Luz Long
   b. shake hands with Luz Long
   c. qualify in the trials
   d. win three gold medals

2. The most important thing that Jesse Owens learned from Luz Long before the third jump was ___.
   a. overcoming fear
   b. remembering his family
   c. clearing the takeoff board
   d. speaking to the crowd

3. In the story, "The Secret Plan," Michael decides to trim the hibiscus bush when he learns that ___.
   a. it caused six accidents
   b. his father read an article
   c. the city wouldn't help
   d. the Hartwells moved away

4. In "The Secret Plan," the club's way of dealing with the Hartwells' bush was to ___.
   a. cut it down
   b. move it to the backyard
   c. call the newspapers
   d. bring it to the clubhouse

5. The article "The Friends of Trees" describes people who learn how to ___.
   a. live in the country
   b. care for city trees
   c. plant young trees
   d. handle a saw

VOCABULARY REVIEW

Review some words from *A Helping Hand*. Choose a word from the list to replace the words in **bold print** in each sentence below. Then write the completed sentences on your paper.

responded	**confident**	**companions**
accomplished	**guardians**	**murmur**

1. When the Olympic games were over, Jesse Owens knew that he had **completed** his highest goals

2. Jesse Owens **reacted** to Luz Long's help by offering his friendship.

3. Linda Jean listened to the **soft sound** of the boys' voices inside the club house.

4. Michael and his **people he spent time with** were determined not to let Linda Jean into the club.

5. The "friends of trees" think of themselves as **protectors** of the city's trees.

6. With the help of Luz Long, Jesse Owens was **certain** that he could qualify for the broad jump.

WRITING ABOUT A HELPING HAND

1. Consider the selections in this unit, and choose the person, or group of people, that gives the most important helping hand, in your opinion. You could choose Luz Long, Michael Cassidy and his friends, or the friends of trees. Write a paragraph explaining the reasons for your choice.

2. The events in "The Third Jump" are told from Jesse Owens' point of view. Write a short story about Owens' three trial jumps from the point of view of someone in the crowd. Describe his first and second jumps. Then describe what seems to be happening between Owens and Long, and the results of Owens' third jump. Describe the reactions from the crowd, including your own reactions. Use details from "The Third Jump" and your own imagination to make your short story interesting.

UNIT

·3·

SOMETHING STRANGE

Things don't always happen the way you expect them to. Sometimes, something happens that doesn't quite make sense. The selections you will read in this unit are about situations where something strange happens.

In the story "The Willing" a boy named Robby thinks he can stop bad things from happening to people by "willing" them not to happen. "The Cold Winds of Summer" is an article about the amazing, snowy summer of 1816 and how it affected people all over the world.

"Odd Things Happen" is an article about a man named Robert Rickard who researches unusual occurences, such as fish falling out of the sky. In the story "The Strange Illness of Mr. Arthur Cook," a man is made sick by his own home, until his daughter, Judy, finds out the mysterious cause of Mr. Cook's illness. This section ends with two poems that tell about a young lady and an old man who each faced a very strange situation.

The articles you will read here explore strange events from real life. The stories and poems give explanations that could only come from a writer's mind. Each of these selections shows that you may not always understand everything that happens, but you should always expect the unexpected.

UNDERSTANDING WORDS IN SENTENCES

Words About Strange Events. Certain words describe strange events, and the ways that people act when strange things happen. Six of those words are in **bold print** in the sentences below. All the words are used in this unit. Use the rest of each sentence to help you choose the correct meaning of each word in **bold print.** Then write the word and its meaning on your paper.

1. Robby's teacher wondered whether he had been seeing things lately and she looked at him **anxiously.**
   (with a slight smile, in a worried way)

2. A **severe** snowstorm in June killed many crops and took all the farmers by surprise.
   (very harsh, causing sudden growth)

3. No one had any clues about the pile of stones that appeared **mysteriously** on a farm in England.
   (all of a sudden, without explanation)

4. The Cooks had no idea how **remarkable** their ordinary-looking new home would turn out to be.
   (unusual, reasonable)

5. Judy wondered why the owners of the house had left quickly and decided to **investigate**.
   (look into to learn the facts, keep a diary)

6. Mrs. Cook was **bewildered** by the change in her husband, but he couldn't seem to explain his actions.
   (amused, puzzled)

"THE WILLING"

Does the power to make things happen really exist? Robby thinks he has this power and can use it to rescue people from danger, but he isn't sure. Find out what happens when Robby decides to test his power once and for all.

WORDS TO KNOW

The words in **bold print** are from "The Willing." Study each word and its meaning carefully.

The pilot asked the passengers to lean forward, as a safety **precaution.**
   precaution — care taken to avoid danger

Robby noticed that there was very little **heartiness** in his father's laughter.
   heartiness — enthusiasm

A **surge** of power went through the engine, and the plane picked up speed.
   surge — strong, sudden increase

It might have been a **coincidence** that the plane recovered after Robby willed it to happen.
   coincidence — things happening together, by chance

The sidewalks were filled with **pedestrians** looking in store windows.
   pedestrians — people walking

Robby's teacher was **astonished** to see him jump to his feet.
   astonished — very surprised, amazed

Robby had stopped listening to people and was **constantly** waiting to use his new power.
   constantly — always

THE WILLING

by ALFRED SLOTE

If it had only happened once, I wouldn't be going public with it. But it happened three times, and so I guess the world ought to know about it.

The first time it happened I was in an airplane with Dad, going down to Cincinnati. It was a nice sunny Saturday. Dad had business in Cincinnati that day and asked me to come along.

We were about ten minutes out of Detroit when the pilot's voice came over the intercom.

"Nothing to be alarmed at, folks," he said, in that pilot kind of twangy voice, "but we seem to be having a problem with one of our engines. So, just to be on the safe side, we're going back to Detroit."

There were lots of groans up and down the aisle that suddenly stopped when we all felt a couple of jolts below the plane.

Dad looked down at me. "This plane could get back on one engine, Robby. Nothing to be worried about."

"Who's worried?" I said.

He had been reading a magazine but stopped. A lot of people had stopped what they were doing — including sleeping.

The plane was turning around, making a long, slow, banking turn.

The pilot came back on the intercom: "We'll be back in Detroit in ten minutes, folks. We're cleared there for a fast, safe landing."

"How does he know?" someone in a seat a few rows back whispered.

Down the aisle came a flight attendant with a bright smile on her face.

"Please buckle your seat belts and take off your shoes," she was telling everyone.

I looked at Dad. "Why do we have to take off our shoes?"

"Darned if I know," Dad said, "but there must be a reason."

I kicked off my sneakers. Outside, the ground was coming up fast. Not like in a movie or anything, but fast enough.

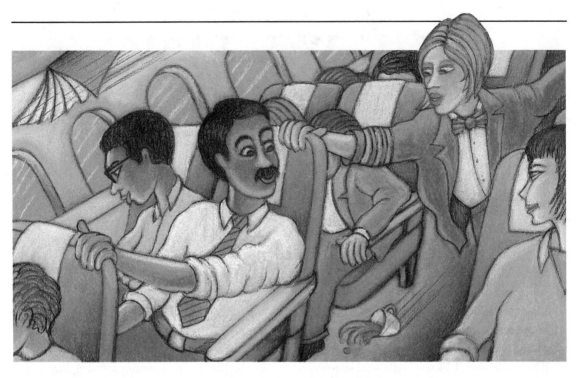

I heard someone in the rear of the plane start to cry. I looked at Dad. He winked at me.

"Nervous Nellie," he said.

"What's to be nervous about?" I said. "We've got our shoes off now."

Dad laughed. He didn't want to laugh, but he did. I didn't want to make him laugh. I sort of wanted to make myself laugh, but didn't.

The pilot's voice came back on. "We're doing fine, folks. Our estimated time of arrival in Detroit is now seven minutes. Just as a precaution, we'll also be asking you to lean forward, face-down."

"That's to see where our shoes are, I guess," I said.

Dad laughed. But there wasn't much heartiness in his laugh.

Now the crying passenger was joined by a few more.

A flight attendant came up the aisle fast, holding onto the tops of seats to keep her balance. "Heads down, please. Please keep your heads down."

I looked out the window. It seemed to me we were almost at the same height as some trees across a field. And just a little above cars on a highway, and going down.

I closed my eyes, and I thought: Come on, plane, start flying upward. Give it gas. Come on, motors. Give it power. Fly, fly, fly.

And that was the first time it happened, and I didn't even think of it as connected with my *willing* it to happen. The jolting below us stopped; we all felt a surge of power go through the plane, speed increased, our nose began to point upward, and we were flying up, almost taking off again.

There was a silence — and then such a cheering. We kept roaring up — back into the sky. People were crying, laughing, clapping.

The pilot's voice came back on with that funny twang: "Well, folks, we don't quite know what happened, but both engines are working again. We'll check it out in Detroit."

But back in Detroit, Dad and I both got off and stayed off.

As I say, I never made the connection between my *willing* that plane back to full power and its coming back to full power. It was a coincidence. I didn't mention it to Dad. Not yet.

But, as things turned out, that was only the first time.

The second time I willed something to happen was when I went Christmas shopping with my grandma. Grandma likes to go to the fancy stores.

We were crossing the street, with the light, and with a policeman there, too . . . when I saw this car double-parked on one side of the street. Lots of cars were double-parked. In fact, it seems to me at times that every car in the city is double-parked. I don't know why this automobile drew my attention, or maybe I do.

There was no driver, the car was running, and a man was sitting in the passenger seat.

The policeman saw it, too, and I saw him walk over to talk to the man. Meanwhile, Grandma and I were still crossing the street. Grandma's 85. A young 85, except when she's crossing streets. So, I had plenty of time to see what happened next.

The policeman must have given the man a strong warning because he slid over to the driver's side, and I guess that was a big mistake. He wasn't a very good driver. He pulled out into the middle of the street with a lurch.

By that time, Grandma and I were across the street and traffic had started again. A taxi cab, coming fast, tried to pull over and let the car out, but it was sandwiched by a bus — and the cab and the car brushed each other — and then came the horrible part.

The car headed for the sidewalk filled with Christmas shoppers.

Everyone saw it happening: the policeman, pedestrians, Grandma, and me. The car wasn't moving fast, but everyone knew it wasn't going to stop, that the man didn't really know how to drive.

The car was going to climb up on the sidewalk and run over everyone there: grown-ups, kids, a Santa Claus with a bell, people walking, people talking, people looking in shop windows. The car was coming at them.

And no one did anything.

I closed my eyes. I did it without thinking. I wasn't remembering the airplane or anything. I just closed my eyes tight and thought: Tires go flat, tires go flat, tires go flat.

There was a tremendous explosion. Just as the car hit the curb, all of its tires exploded, and the car rocked there for a moment. Then someone on the sidewalk jumped in and turned off the engine.

And then, just as it had been in the airplane, there was cheering and crying and laughing. Grandma took my hand. "I've never been so frightened in my life, Robby," she said.

"I wasn't," I said.

She looked at me strangely. But the truth was, I wasn't frightened. And I suddenly realized that I hadn't been frightened in the airplane, either.

And when I thought of the airplane, I realized that *I* had made that plane's engine recover, just as I had blown those tires out.

I had closed my eyes and, without thinking, *willed* those things to happen.

Standing there with my grandmother, I realized I had power inside me that I didn't know existed.

I could prevent accidents.

That was the second time. And still I told no one about it. Not even Dad. I knew he wouldn't believe it. He might even think I'd flipped or something.

But I had the power—and I waited for the next accident to happen. I *wanted* the next accident to happen.

And, of course, it didn't. I mean, the whole point of accidents is that you don't know they're going to happen. You can't walk to school waiting for a car to run someone over or an airplane to fall from the sky or a live electric wire to fall on someone.

But that's what I did. I'd walk to school with my friend Timmy Wilson, and Timmy would say to me: "You okay, Robby?"

"Sure I'm okay."

"You keep looking around. I asked you if you wanted to have a game of catch this afternoon, but you didn't answer me. You keep looking at that oil truck there."

"Pumping oil into houses can be dangerous," I said, keeping a good eye on the oil line.

Timmy just stared at me.

Then, in school, in our unit on explorers, Mrs. Silkworth was talking about how someone was looking for the fountain of youth in Florida long before our grandparents went down there every winter, and I looked out the window and there was this old man walking through the park (our school is at one end of the park) and there were two big dogs chasing each other. They were there almost every day. They weren't near the old man, but they could spot him and they could attack him . . . any second. I rose to my feet.

"Robby, are you all right?" Mrs. Silkworth asked, astonished.

"Wait a second," I said, looking out the window.

The dogs saw the old man. I waited. The dogs ran away, still chasing each other. The old man kept on walking. I sighed and sat down.

"Perhaps you might want to go down and see the school nurse, Robby," Mrs. Silkworth said anxiously.

"What for?" I said. "There's nothing wrong with me."

But, of course, there was. My folks noticed it, too. I had stopped listening to people. I was constantly on the lookout. I felt I had to have at least one more proof of my new power . . .

and then I could go public with it.

But nothing happened. Arborville, Michigan, seemed to be free of troubles and accidents . . . at least while I was around.

It was June when I made my move, or my big mistake, as it turned out. I couldn't stand waiting any longer for an accident, so I decided to *will* one into happening — and then prevent it.

First, though, I needed a victim I could save. Who should it be? An adult or a kid?

I decided on a kid. A kid who would always be grateful to me. I decided it would be Carolyn Brown, who lived over on Olivia Street.

Why did I choose her as my victim? First, because she was pretty. Second, because I thought she might like me. Third, because her family had a big swimming pool in their backyard, and I couldn't count the times Timmy Wilson and I had walked by their house on hot July afternoons, wishing Carolyn would invite us over for a swim.

Well, this ought to do it.

But what should the accident be? And where? Where depended on what, I figured. And I figured it would have to be either inside school or just outside because those were really the only places I ever saw Carolyn.

Maybe those two big dogs. They played in the park every afternoon. They were really friendly dogs, but if I *willed* them into anger just as Carolyn was stepping out the front door of the school, and then willed them into running at her . . .

Give it a try, I thought. There's nothing to lose and a swimming pool to gain.

I thought all that out on Monday. On Tuesday, I got out early and checked the park. Sure enough, the dogs were there frisking about. Kids were pouring out the front door and the side door. It would not work if Carolyn came out the side door.

So I *willed* her out the front door. And sure enough, out she came, talking to someone. (I think this might have been a coincidence. She usually came out the front door.)

Now she was walking down the walk to the main crosswalk. At the main crosswalk, she would turn left and walk toward Olivia Street.

The two dogs were about 100 feet away, not even looking at her. I was standing alone near the kindergarten's jungle gym, just off to the side, where I could control things beautifully.

The girl Carolyn was walking with turned right. Carolyn turned left. Okay, accident, I thought, happen!

I closed my eyes. Dogs run at Carolyn, dogs run at Carolyn, dogs run at Carolyn . . . I *willed* it over and over and then looked.

I got the goose pimples again. The dogs had stopped playing with each other. They looked at Carolyn, and here they came: fast, and growling, and with teeth bared. They came running at her. Someone saw them and yelled for Carolyn to run.

She started to run.

I closed my eyes and *willed*: Dogs chase something else, dogs chase something else, dogs chase a cat!

I opened my eyes. The dogs had changed direction. A brown cat had appeared, and they

were chasing the cat. The cat was running for its life.

And the direction *it* was running in was right toward me. No, I thought, Oh no . . .

But it happened before I could close my eyes and do any *willing* . The cat leaped into my arms for safety, and the dogs came after it and me. There was nowhere for me to run, no tree to climb, only the kindergarten jungle gym I was standing next to.

And that's what I did. I climbed the kindergarten jungle gym with a cat in my arms and the dogs leaping and growling at my rear end. I would have closed my eyes and *willed* the dogs away, but it's tough to climb a jungle gym with your eyes closed and a cat in your arms.

The dogs barked their heads off until someone fetched their owner, who later got a stiff fine from the police for letting his dogs run loose. Everyone cheered my act of "bravery" in saving the poor pussycat. And no one cheered any louder than Carolyn.

"Robby," she said, "you were wonderful."

And the next day she invited me to go swimming in her pool!

It looks like this summer I'll be a regular visitor at the Browns' pool, where I'll keep an eye out to prevent accidents, but I sure won't *will* any to happen. That, as I said, was a big mistake.

Dad, to whom I finally told this story, doesn't believe a word of it. He says I ought to save my talent for really big things like stopping runaway freight trains or preventing a dam from bursting.

He's kidding, of course, but I'm not. I'm ready — and willing. ◆

READING CHECK

Answer the following questions about "The Willing." You may want to check your answers by reviewing details in the story.

1. Why was Robby on an airplane with his father? What did the pilot announce to the passengers?

2. What did Robby tell the plane to do when he closed his eyes?

3. Where was Robby the second time he willed something to happen? What did he do when he saw the car moving toward the sidewalk?

4. After the close call with the car, what did Robby believe he had the power to do?

5. Why did Robby begin acting strangely? Which people noticed that?

6. Whom did Robby choose as an accident victim? What kind of accident did he try to arrange?

7. Why did Robby's plan put him in danger? What invitation did Robby get at the end of the story?

WHAT DO YOU THINK?

1. Do you think Robby was really able to make things happen by willing them? Explain. Why did he think he could?

2. Why did Robby take such a big chance in putting Carolyn Smith in danger? If Robby had told his plan to you, would you have tried to talk him out of doing it? How?

3. What would you do if you saw a small child about to do something dangerous, such as run into the street?

VOCABULARY CHECK

Read the following sentences and choose the correct meaning of each word in **bold print.** Then write each word and its meaning on your paper.

1. What a relief it must have been to feel the **surge** of power in the plane.
   (sudden increase, sharp drop)

2. Robby was **constantly** on the look out for an accident to happen.
   (sadly, always)

3. It's a sensible **precaution** to stay out of reach when chased by angry dogs.
   (care taken to avoid danger, way of training animals)

4. The **heartiness** of the applause showed the feelings of the crowd.
   (softness, enthusiasm)

5. It was just a **coincidence** that Carolyn came out as Robby was passing by.
   (lucky break, things happening together by chance)

6. Several **pedestrians** had a narrow escape from the speeding car.
   (people walking, people driving)

7. Robby was **astonished** when the cat leaped into his arms.
   (delighted, amazed)

STRATEGY CHECK

The paragraph below is based on the story "The Willing." Choose the correct word to fill in each blank. Use the rest of the paragraph and your knowledge of the story to help you. Then write the whole paragraph on your paper.

Robbie was on an airplane with his f____. Suddenly, the voice of the p____ came over the intercom. The passengers were told about a problem with one e____. The plane seemed about to cr____ to the ground. Robbie willed the plane to come back to full p____. The plane then l____ safely in Detroit.

◆ INTRODUCING ◆

"THE COLD WINDS OF SUMMER"

In the summer, the weather warms up. You can usually count on that. But during the summer of 1816, strange things began to happen to the weather and to the lives of many people. Read the true story of this most unusual summer.

WORDS TO KNOW

The words in **bold print** are from "The Cold Winds of Summer." Study each word and its meaning carefully.

Icicles up to a foot long hung from the **eaves** of the house.
   eaves — the lower edges of a roof

After the crops failed, hungry people went **scavenging** in the woods for food.
   scavenging — searching for anything that can be found

The cold summer caused a **famine** in many parts of the world because crops died.
   famine — great lack of food

The **epidemic** of disease killed many people who were already weak from hunger.
   epidemic — fast spreading of a disease to many people

Now, even if cold weather kills the crops, **surplus** food can be brought to places that need it.
   surplus — extra

It would matter less today if the **global** temperature dropped a few degrees.
   global — of the whole world

THE COLD WINDS OF SUMMER

by L.G. SHERMAN

All night long the wind howled, and sleet and hail beat against the windows. In the morning there was snow on the mountains, and icicles up to a foot long hung from the eaves. For the next few days, the cold and snow continued. Was it a typical week in November? That is what the people of New England must have thought in June, 1816. Their crops froze in the fields, and the leaves on the trees, still glowing with the yellow-green of spring, turned black.

A man named Chauncey Jerome of Plymouth, Connecticut, wrote these words back then:

I well remember the seventh of June. While on my way to work, about a mile from home, dressed throughout with thick woolen clothes and an overcoat on, my hands got so cold that I was obliged to lay down my tools and put on a pair of mittens that I had in my pocket. It snowed about an hour that day. On the tenth of June, my wife brought in some clothes that had been spread on the ground the night before, which were frozen stiff as in winter.

From Connecticut to the Canadian province of Quebec, farmers planted their crops again. In some places there was not enough seed to replant, so they had to make do with smaller crops. The warm weather returned, and by July corn and wheat covered the fields with short green stems. But on the fifth of July, another freezing storm hit. It killed all the corn, except what was planted in fields protected in some way from the icy blast. It was not until July 12 that the summer weather returned, and by then there was very little seed corn for starting again. Luckily, this cold snap was

less severe than the one in June, and much of the wheat and grain crops in the New England states survived.

In Canada, however, the July storm destroyed not only corn crops, but the wheat crops as well. A newspaper article pointed out that many poor people, who lived mainly on bread and milk, now had no bread.

If the rest of the summer had been normal, the remaining corn would have ripened and the wheat would have been harvested. But on August 21, another killing frost was felt in northern New England and Canada. The crops due to be harvested in two weeks were destroyed once again. Corn, potatoes, and beans were lost in Maine, Massachusetts, and New Hampshire. Farmers farther south were struck by the next frost, which arrived on August 30. Newspapers began calling the year 1816 "Eighteen Hundred and Froze to Death."

Not just New England and Canada were affected by the unusually cold weather. All over the world, people noticed that the daily temperatures were the lowest they'd been since the earliest records. In France, people were so hungry that they went scavenging in the woods for food. In India, there was a terrible famine.

What could have caused such a freak summer? Many scientists believe that the cold wave started in April, 1815, when a volcano on the tiny island of Sumbawa in Indonesia blew its top. In the world's greatest eruption in 400 years, Mount Tambora lost 4,200 feet in height, throwing huge clouds of dust into the air all at once. The clouds were so dense that islands within 300 miles were in complete darkness for three days.

Most of the volcanic dust did not settle down, but was carried into the upper atmosphere and spread out around the earth. There it formed a layer that reflected sunlight back out into space. Only a small part of the sun's usual light was lost this way, but it was enough to lower the average temperature several degrees and make the unusual summer storms possible.

And so a volcano in the South Pacific caused the cold temperatures and the lost crops around the world. But there were other effects, too. Naturally, the first problem was that there were not enough food crops to last the winter and many people went hungry. For people who were already tired of their rocky New England soil, this summer was the last straw. During the next few years, they began to move west in greater numbers.

But there were still other effects. Some scientists believe that the eruption of 1815 caused the outbreaks of cholera in the 1830s. Cholera is a disease that is spread by using dirty water for drinking and cooking. A terrible epidemic of cholera began in India in 1816. Of course, in India there was also the famine of the cold summer. People who were already weakened by hunger could not withstand the illness. The British army that controlled India spread the cholera to other countries in Asia. By 1832,

cholera had reached the cities of Moscow and Paris, and had even crossed the Atlantic to the Canadian city of Montreal. One hundred people a day were dying of cholera in New York City by the end of July, 1832. Luckily, people discovered what was causing the disease to spread and started to clean up their water.

As many as 12,000 people may have died on the island when Tambora erupted, 70,000 more in the worldwide famine that followed, and countless others because of the cholera epidemic. What would happen today if there were another eruption like Mount Tambora's?

First of all, modern scientists are usually able to predict when a volcano is about to erupt, so that people living nearby can be moved to safety before the explosion. Also, cleanliness and the treatment of disease have improved greatly over the past century.

Even if there were crop failures in some places, we are now able to store food in warehouses. We can also get information about other parts of the world within minutes, so surplus food could be moved to the places that needed it most.

Finally, it would matter less today if the global temperatures dropped a few degrees because the world's temperature has risen slightly over the last 100 years.

There may be some summer days in the future when the temperature drops and the wind howls. There may even be some snow. But chances are that there will never be another summer like the summer of 1816. ◆

READING CHECK

Answer the following questions about "The Cold Winds of Summer." You may want to check your answers by reviewing details in the article.

1. What happened to the crops and trees in New England after a storm in June 1816? Which crop was almost wiped out on the fifth of July? Why?

2. Why was the loss of the wheat crop so important in Canada?

3. Which two countries outside the United States and Canada were badly hurt by the cold weather? What happened in those countries?

4. What do scientists think was the cause of the freak summer?

5. Where did many people in New England go after the summer of 1816?

6. What were two serious problems caused around the world by the cold weather?

7. What is one reason that cold weather in the summer would be less serious now?

WHAT DO YOU THINK?

1. Why do you think the farmers in New England couldn't protect their crops from the cold? Is it always possible to protect crops from sudden cold weather today? Explain.

2. What would happen in your neighborhood if snow fell for a week in the middle of the summer? What changes would you make in your daily activities?

3. Do you believe that bad weather can always be predicted ahead of time nowadays? Explain.

VOCABULARY CHECK

Read the following sentences and choose the correct meaning of each word in **bold print**. Then write each word and its meaning on your paper.

1. In France, people had so little to eat that they went **scavenging** for food.
    (planting, searching)

2. Those people with **surplus** food could share it with others in need.
    (extra, cooked)

3. The cold rain dripped off the **eaves** onto the ground.
    (low branches of trees, lower edges of a roof)

4. The **famine** made people so weak that they became sick easily.
    (great lack of food, clouds of dust)

5. Illness spread so fast that it became a **global** problem.
    (dangerous, worldwide)

6. An **epidemic** of cholera is only one of the terrible things that happened in 1816.
    (dose of medicine, fast spreading of disease)

STRATEGY CHECK

The paragraph below is based on the article "The Cold Winds of Summer." Choose the correct word to fill in each blank. Use the rest of the paragraph and what you remember about the article to help you. Then write the whole paragraph on your paper.

In the summer of 1816, there was cold and sn____. The crops fr____ in the fields. When farmers planted their cr____ again, more freezing weather killed most of them. That strange summer was cold all over the w____, not just in the United States and Canada. A volcano in the South Pacific c____ the cold temperatures. There will probably never be another s____ like the one in 1816.

"ODD THINGS HAPPEN"

Everyone knows that odd things happen. Sometimes the odd things are never explained. In this article you will read about a man who collects stories of strange events that seem to have no cause. As you read the article, decide how you would explain the odd things that happen.

WORDS TO KNOW

The words in **bold print** are from "Odd Things Happen." Study each word and its meaning carefully.

Robert Rickard's house is **crammed** with reports of strange events.
    crammed — packed full

Rickard does not **resist** the truth when he hears it.
    resist — refuse to accept, fight against

Some newspapers may **exaggerate** things to make them seem more exciting.
    exaggerate — make greater than the truth

Rickard hears many reports of **meteorites** falling from the sky.
    meteorites — lumps of metal or stone that fall from space to the earth

The fish that fell from the sky were **evidence** that something strange had happened.
    evidence — proof

The fish were **commonly** found in a river two miles from the house.
    commonly — usually

ODD THINGS HAPPEN

by BARRY NEWMAN

Odd things happen. For instance: In 1980, a shower of peas fell on Trevor Williams in Wales, Great Britain.

"I was cleaning out the goldfish pond in the garden," said Williams. "It was a clear, beautiful day. I heard this plop, plop, and the next thing I knew, a real good shower of peas came down. Dried peas."

How strange, thought Williams. He called the local radio station and reported the event. Then the story appeared in newspapers, and it was noticed by Robert Rickard. When odd things happen, Robert Rickard takes note.

Rickard collects accounts of unexplained events. His house in London is crammed with reports of strange happenings.

A few years ago, Rickard heard about the piles of small stones that appeared mysteriously on a farm in England. The farmer thought that worms had built the stone piles. But Rickard did not accept that explanation. Nor did he have any other explanation. Robert Rickard doesn't explain things; he records them.

"I think of myself as a clerk, filing all these things away," he says. "I have no urge to believe in explanations. If something drops out of the sky, I'm not surprised; I'm interested."

A report of a toad found in a chunk of coal stirred Rickard's interest. So did the news that a bald farmer began to grow hair again after a cow licked his scalp.

Every few months, Robert Rickard writes about strange happenings for the magazine he owns, *Fortean Times*. The magazine is named after Charles Fort, an American who spent much of his life collecting instances of the unexplained and

noting each one on a scrap of paper.

Like Fort, Rickard keeps an open mind about the causes of strange happenings. But he doesn't resist scientific truths. After his magazine published a story about a "wildman" in China, the creature turned out to be a rhesus monkey. Rickard printed a correction.

Rickard gets most of his information from newspapers, but he knows that some newspapers are likely to exaggerate things. That is why he has a special interest in physical events, such as things falling from the sky.

Rocks fall from the sky all the time. (They are called meteorites.) A turtle encased in ice fell to the ground in Mississippi in 1894. In 1969, there was a rain of golf balls in Florida, and four years later, several thousand toads landed on a village in France. Rickard also has records of nuts and bolts, nails, cookies, and pennies falling out of the heavens.

One time there was a fish-fall in

Rickard's own neighborhood. On the night of May 27, 1984, four flounders, three whitings, and five smelts fell into the backyard of the Langtons' house. Several more fish hit the roof. Ron Langton and his wife, Ellen, were watching television at the time. It was raining.

"We heard things smacking down," Ron Langton said. The next morning, they found the fish.

Robert Rickard heard about the fish-fall. He visited the scene and carried the evidence to the Natural History Museum. The fish, he was told, were commonly found in the Thames River, two miles from the Langtons' house. They could have been picked up by a tornado.

Rickard called the London Weather Center and the coast guard. He learned that conditions were all wrong for tornados on the night of the fish-fall.

Robert Rickard can't explain the fish in the Langtons' backyard. He only knows that odd things do happen. ◆

READING CHECK

Answer the following questions about "Odd Things Happen." You may want to check your answers by reviewing details in the story.

1. Why did the shower of peas attract the attention of Robert Rickard?

2. What does Rickard do with the strange stories when he first collects them? Where does he print some of the stories?

3. Where does Rickard get most of his information?

4. What are four things that fell from the sky before 1984?

5. How did Rickard know that the falling fish could not have been carried by a tornado?

WHAT DO YOU THINK?

1. What do you think could be an explanation for the shower of peas, the fish-fall, or any of the other strange things described in the article?

2. Why do you think Robert Rickard does not find it necessary to explain all the odd things that happen?

3. Would you call Robert Rickard a scientist? Why, or why not?

VOCABULARY CHECK

Read the following sentences and choose the correct meaning of each word in **bold print.** Then write each word and its meaning on your paper.

1. Dried peas falling into a pond were **evidence** that something strange had happened.
   (proof, reports)

2. People often report that they have seen **meteorites** in the night sky.
   (lumps of stone falling to earth , planets)

3. Robert Rickard has to be careful that people don't **exaggerate** their reports of odd things happening.
   (write an opinion, make greater than the truth)

4. Rickard can never **resist** reading an article about mysterious events.
   (fight against, make a start on)

5. The newspaper is **crammed** with information about strange events.
   (colored in, packed full)

6. Toads, nails, and pennies do not **commonly** fall from the sky.
   (rapidly, usually)

STRATEGY CHECK

The paragraph below is based on the article "Odd Things Happen." Choose the correct word to fill in each blank. Use the rest of the paragraph and your knowledge of the article to help you. Then write the whole paragraph on your paper.

    It is true that odd things do h____. Robert Rickard reports many strange events in a m____ called *Fortean Times.* He has heard many tales of odd things falling from the s____. Golf balls, toads, and even three kinds of f____ have landed on the ground. Rickard once heard a st____ of an ice-covered turtle that fell to the ground in Mississippi. Rickard never tries to explain these events; he just r____ them.

◆ INTRODUCING ◆

"THE STRANGE ILLNESS OF MR. ARTHUR COOK"

Mr. and Mrs. Cook never guessed that their new home in the country would bring so many problems. But right from the beginning, Judy Cook knows there's something strange about the house. And then her father comes down with a mysterious illness. It's up to Judy to find an explanation.

WORDS TO KNOW

The words in **bold print** are from "The Strange Illness of Mr. Arthur Cook." Study each word and its meaning carefully.

The Cooks did not seem to mind that the house was small and looked rather **bleak.**
    bleak — cold and gloomy

Judy's habit of asking questions made her the most **inquisitive** member of her family.
    inquisitive — curious, full of questions

The garden had been **neglected** and was filled with weeds.
    neglected — left without care

Judy asked so many questions that many people found her **tiresome.**
    tiresome — annoying, boring

Mrs. Baxter's touch on Judy's arm was soft, but **insistent.**
    insistent — firm, determined

THE STRANGE ILLNESS OF MR. ARTHUR COOK

by PHILIPPA PEARCE

On a cold, shiny day at the end of winter, the Cook family went to look at the house they were likely to buy. Mr. and Mrs. Cook had visited it several times before, and had discussed it thoroughly. This was a first visit for their children, Judy and Mike.

Also with the Cooks was Mr. Biley, of the real estate agent's firm of Ketch, Robb, and Biley in Walchester.

"Why has *he* come?" whispered Judy. (Although the Cooks didn't know this, Mr. Biley did not usually accompany clients in order to clinch deals.)

Her parents shushed Judy.

They had driven a little way out of Walchester into the country. The car now turned down a lane which, perhaps 50 years before, had been hardly more than a farm trail. Now there were several houses along it. The lane came to a dead end at a house with a *For Sale* sign at its front gate. On the gate itself was the name of the house: Southcroft.

"There it is!" said Mr. Arthur Cook to his two children.

"And very nice, too!" Mr. Biley said enthusiastically.

But, in fact, the house was not really nice. It was small to medium, made of brick, and with a slate roof. It was exactly rectangular, and rather bleak-looking. It stood in the middle of a large garden, also exactly rectangular and rather bleak-looking.

Mike, who tended to like most things

that happened to him, said, "Seems okay." He was gazing not only at the house and its garden, but at the quiet lane — ideal for his bike — and at the surrounding countryside. It would be far, far better than where they were living now, in Walchester.

Judy, who was older than Mike, and the only one in the family with an inquisitive nose, said nothing — yet. She looked around alertly.

"Nice big garden for kids to play in," Mr. Biley pointed out.

"I might even grow a few vegetables," said Mr. Cook.

"Oh, Arthur!" his wife said, laughing.

"Well," Mr. Cook said defensively, "I haven't had much chance up to now, have I?" In Walchester, the Cooks had only a paved backyard. But, anyway, Mr. Cook, whose job was installing television antennas on roofs, had always said that in his spare time he wanted to be indoors in a comfortable chair.

"Anyway," said Mr. Biley, as they went in by the front gate, "you've got good soil here."

They reached the front door. Mr. Biley unlocked it, and they all trooped in.

Southcroft had probably been built some time between the two world wars. There was nothing of special interest about it. On the other hand, it seemed to be well kept.

The Cooks went everywhere and looked everywhere. Their footsteps echoed in empty rooms. They came together in the living room, which had French windows opening onto the garden at the back. Tactfully, Mr. Biley withdrew into the garden to leave the family to its private talk.

"Well, there you are," said Mr. Cook. "Just our size house. Not remarkable in any way, but snug, I think."

"Remarkable in one way, Arthur," said his wife. "Remarkably cheap."

"Yes," agreed Mr. Cook.

"Why is it so cheap?" asked Judy.

"You ask too many questions beginning with *why* ," said her father, but good-humoredly.

It was true, however, that there seemed no special reason for the house to be so cheap. Odd, perhaps.

Mike and Judy went out into the garden, and Mr. Biley came in again.

There wasn't much for the children to see in the garden. Close to the house grew unkempt grass, with a big, old apple tree — the only tree in the garden. The rest of the garden had been tended, but now it was neglected, a mess of dead weeds. There were some straggly bushes. There was a garden shed, and behind it a mass of stuff which Judy left Mike to investigate. She wanted to get back to the adult conversation.

By the time Judy rejoined the group indoors, there was no doubt about it: The Cooks were buying the house. Mr. Biley was extremely pleased, Judy noticed. He caught Judy staring at him and pleasantly, but very unwisely, said, "Well, young lady?"

Judy, invited to join in the conversation, had a great many questions to ask. She knew she wouldn't be allowed to ask them all, and she began almost at random: "Who used to live here?"

"A family called Cribble," said Mr. Biley. "A very *nice* family called Cribble."

"Cribble," Judy repeated to herself, storing the piece of information away. "And why—"

At that moment Mike walked in again from the garden. "There's lots of stuff behind the shed," he said. "Rolls and rolls of chicken wire, in an awful mess, and wood — posts and slats and stuff."

"Easily cleared," said Mr. Biley. "The previous owners were going to breed dogs, I believe. They would have built sheds, dog runs — all that kind of thing."

"Why did the Cribbles give up the idea?" asked Judy.

Mr. Biley looked uneasy. "Not the Cribbles," he said, "the Johnsons. The family here before the Cribbles."

"Why did the Johnsons give up the idea, then?" asked Judy. "I mean, when they'd gotten all the stuff for it?"

"They —" Mr. Biley appeared to think deeply. "They had to move rather unexpectedly."

"Why?"

"Family reasons, perhaps?" said Mrs. Cook quickly. She knew some people found Judy tiresome.

"Family reasons, no doubt," Mr. Biley agreed.

Judy said thoughtfully to herself: "The Johnsons didn't stay long enough to start dog-breeding, and they went in such a hurry that they left their stuff behind. The Cribbles came, but they didn't stay long enough to have time to clear away all the Johnsons' stuff. I wonder why *they* left . . . "

Nobody could say that Judy was asking Mr. Biley a question, but he answered her all the same. "My dear young lady," he said, in a manner so polite it was also rude, "I do not know why. Nor is it my business." He sounded as if he did not think it was Judy's, either. He turned his back on her and began talking loudly to Mr. Cook about the sale of the house.

Judy was not put out. She had investigated mysteries and secrets before this, and she knew that patience was all important.

The Cooks bought Southcroft and moved in almost at once. Spring came late that year, and in the cold weather the house proved snug. When the frosts were over, the family did some work outside, getting rid of all the dog-breeding junk. They made a fine bonfire of the wood. Mr. Cook took a long look at the weeds beginning to sprout everywhere, and groaned. He bought a garden fork and a spade and hoe and rake and put them in the shed.

In their different ways, the Cooks were satisfied with the move. The new house was still convenient for Mr. Cook's work. Mrs. Cook found that the neighbors kept to themselves more than she would have liked, but she got a part-time job in a shop in the village.

Mike made new friends in the new school, and they went riding around the countryside on their bikes. Judy was slower at making friends, partly because she was absorbed in her own affairs, especially in investigation. In this, she was disappointed for a time.

She could find out so little about the Cribbles and the Johnsons: why they had stayed so briefly at Southcroft; why they had moved in such a hurry. The Cribbles now lived on the other side of Walchester, in a house with a large garden which they had had landscaped. (Perhaps the size of the garden at Southcroft had attracted them to the house in the first place. In the village, people said that the Cribbles had already hired landscape experts for Southcroft, when they suddenly decided to leave.) As for the Johnsons, Judy discovered that they had moved right away, to Yorkshire, to do their dog-breeding. Before the Cribbles and the Johnsons, an old couple called Baxter had lived in the house for many years, until one had died and the other moved away.

The Cooks had settled in. Spring brought sunshine and longer days. It also brought the first symptoms of Mr. Cook's strange illness.

At first, the trouble seemed to be his eyesight. He complained of a kind of brownish fog between himself and the television screen. He couldn't see clearly enough to enjoy the programs. He thought he noticed that this fogginess was worse when he was watching in daylight on the weekends or in early evening. He tried to deal with this by drawing the curtains in the room where the television set was, but the fogginess persisted.

Mr. Cook went to an optician to see whether he needed glasses. The optician did all the usual tests, and said that Mr. Cook's vision seemed excellent. Mr. Cook said it wasn't — or, at least, sometimes wasn't. The optician said that eyesight could be affected by a person's state of general health, and suggested that, if the trouble continued, Mr. Cook should see a doctor.

Mr. Cook was annoyed at the time he had wasted at the optician's, and went home to try to enjoy his favorite Saturday afternoon program. Not only did he suffer from increased fogginess of vision, but he developed a splitting headache. In the end, he switched the television set off and went outside and dug savagely in the garden, uprooting a great number of weeds. By late afternoon, he had cleared a large patch, in which Judy planted radishes and cress.

At the end of an afternoon's digging, the headache had gone. Mr. Cook was also able to watch the late-night movie on television without discomfort. But his Saturday as a whole had been ruined. When he went to bed, his sleep was troubled by strange dreams, and on Sunday morning he woke at first light. This had become the pattern of his sleeping recently: haunted dreams and early wakings. He couldn't get to sleep

again and he spent the rest of Sunday —a breezy, sunny day — moving restlessly about indoors from Sunday paper to television set, saying he felt awful.

Mrs. Cook said that perhaps he ought to see a doctor, as the optician had advised. Mr. Cook shouted at her that he wouldn't. But, as spring turned to summer, it became clear that something would have to be done. Mr. Cook's condition was worsening. He gave up trying to watch television. Regularly, he got up at sunrise because he couldn't sleep longer and couldn't even rest in bed. (Sometimes he went out and dug in the garden and, when he did so, the exercise or the fresh air seemed to make him feel better, at least for the time being.) He lost his appetite, and he was always irritable. He grumbled at Mike for being out so much on his bicycle, and he grumbled at Judy for being at home. Her investigations no longer amused him at all. Judy had pointed out that his illness seemed to vary with the weather: nice days made it worse. She wondered why.

At last Mrs. Cook burst out that she could stand this no longer: "Arthur, you *must* go to the doctor." As though he had only been waiting for someone to insist, Mr. Cook agreed.

The doctor listened carefully to Mr. Cook's account of his symptoms and examined him thoroughly. The doctor said he thought Mr. Cook's condition might be the result of nervous tension. "Anything worrying you?" asked the doctor.

"Of course there is!" exploded Mr. Cook. "I'm ill, aren't I? I'm worried sick about that!"

The doctor asked if there was anything else that Mr. Cook worried about: His wife? His children? His job?

"I lie awake in the morning and worry about them all," said Mr. Cook. "And about that huge garden in that awful state . . . "

"What garden?"

"Our garden. It's huge and it's gone wild and I ought to get it in order, I suppose, and — oh, I don't know! I'm no gardener."

"Perhaps you shouldn't have a garden that size," suggested the doctor. "Perhaps you should consider moving into a house with no garden, or at least a small one. Somewhere, say, in Walchester."

"That's what we moved *from*," said Mr. Cook. "Less than six months ago."

"Oh!" said the doctor. He called Mrs. Cook into his office and suggested that her husband might be suffering from overwork. The doctor suggested a week off, to see what *that* would do.

That week marked the climax of Mr. Cook's illness. It drove Mrs. Cook nearly out of her wits, and it drove Judy to urgent inquiries.

The week came at the very beginning of June, an ideal month in which to try to recover from overwork. Judy and Mike were at school all day, so everything was quiet at home for their father. The sun shone, and Mr. Cook planned to sit outside in a deck chair and catch up on lost sleep. Then,

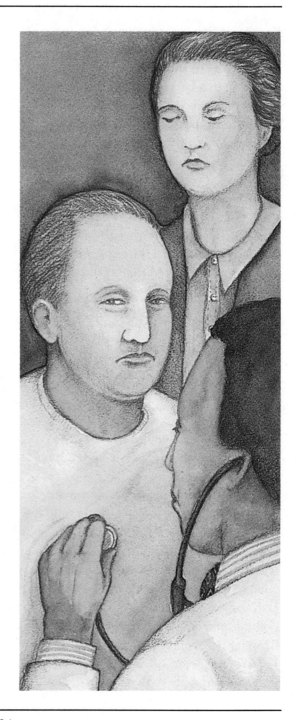

when the children came home, he would go to bed early with the portable television set. (He assumed that rest would help deal with the foggy vision.)

Things did not work out like that at all. During that week, Mr. Cook was seized with a terrible restlessness. It seemed impossible for him to get any rest at all. He tried only once to watch television, and Judy noticed that afterward he seemed almost afraid. He was a shadow of his former self when, at the end of the week, he went back to work.

After he had left the house that morning, Mrs. Cook spoke her fears: "It'll be the hospital next, I know. Oh, why did we ever come to live here!"

"You think it's something to do with the house?" asked Judy.

"Well, your dad was perfectly all right before. I'd say there was something wrong with the drains here, but there's no smell; and, anyway, why should only he fall ill?"

"There is something wrong with the house," said Judy. "I couldn't ask the Johnsons about it, so I asked the Cribbles."

"The Cribbles! The family we bought the house from?"

"Yes. They live on the other side of Walchester. I went there —"

"Oh, Judy!" said her mother. "You'll get yourself into trouble with your questions, one of these days."

"No, I won't," said Judy. "I went to ask them about this house. I rang the bell and Mrs. Cribble answered. At least, I think it must have been Mrs. Cribble. She was quite nice. I told her my name, but I don't think she connected me with buying the house from them. Then I asked her about the house, whether *they* had noticed anything."

"And what did she say?"

"She didn't say anything. She slammed the door in my face."

"Oh, Judy!" cried Mrs. Cook, and burst into tears.

Her mother's tears decided Judy; she would confront Mr. Biley himself, of Ketch, Robb, and Biley. She was not so innocent as to think he would give a young girl an interview. But if she could buttonhole him somewhere, she might get at least one useful piece of information.

After school that day, Judy presented herself at the offices of Ketch, Robb, and Biley in Walchester. She had her question ready. "Has my father been in to see Mr. Biley yet?" she asked. That sounded respectable. The receptionist said that Mr. Biley was talking with a client, and that she really couldn't say —

"I'll wait," said Judy, like a good girl.

Judy waited. She was prepared to wait until the offices shut at 5:30, when Mr. Biley would surely leave to go home. But much earlier than that, Mr. Biley came downstairs with someone who seemed to be an important client. Mr. Biley showed him to the door, chatting in the jovial way that Judy remembered so well. They said good-bye at the door, and parted, and Mr. Biley started back into the office.

Judy caught up with him and laid a hand on his arm: "Mr. Biley — please!"

Mr. Biley turned. He did not recognize Judy. He smiled. "Yes, young lady?"

"We bought Southcroft from the Cribbles." she began.

Mr. Biley's smile vanished instantly. He said, "I should make clear at once that Ketch, Robb, and Biley will not, under any circumstances, handle that property again."

"Why?" asked Judy. She couldn't help asking.

"The sale of the same property three times in 18 months may bring income to us, but it does not bring reputation. So I wish you good day."

Judy said, "*Please*, I only need to ask you one thing, really." She gripped the cloth of his sleeve.

"Well? Be quick," he said.

"Before the Cribbles and the Johnsons, there were the Baxters. When Mr. Baxter died, where did Mrs. Baxter move to?"

"Into Senior House, Waddington Road." He removed Judy's fingers from his coat sleeve. "Remember to tell your father *not* to call Ketch, Robb, and Biley for the resale of the property. Good-bye."

It was getting late, but Judy thought she should finish the job. She found a telephone booth and called her mother to say she was going to see Mrs. Baxter on Waddington Road. She was glad that her telephone time ran out before her mother could say much in reply.

Then she set off for Waddington Road.

By the time she reached the apartment building, Judy felt tired, thirsty, and hungry. There was no problem about seeing Mrs. Baxter. The porter said the residents had just finished seeing a film on mountaineering in the Alps. He told her the number of Mrs. Baxter's apartment, and said Mrs. Baxter would probably be starting her tea.

Judy found the door and knocked. A delicious smell of hot-buttered toast seemed to be coming through the keyhole. A thin little voice told her to come in. And there sat Mrs. Baxter behind a teapot, spreading honey on a piece of buttered toast.

"Oh," said Judy, faintly.

Mrs. Baxter was delighted to have a visitor. "Sit down, dear, and I'll get a glass of milk and another plate of toast."

She was a nice woman, with gingery-gray hair — she wore a gingery dress almost to match — and dark eyes.

Mrs. Baxter brought milk and some extra toast. All this without asking Judy her name or her business.

"Jelly on your toast?" asked Mrs. Baxter.

"Yes, please," said Judy. "I'm Judy Cook, Mrs. Baxter."

"Oh, yes? I'll have to get the jar of jelly. I don't use jelly myself, you know."

She walked over to some shelves. She had her back to Judy, but Judy could see her hands reaching up to a jar of jelly.

"Mrs. Baxter, we live in the house you used to live in, Southcroft."

Mrs. Baxter's hands never reached the jelly jar, but stayed up in the air for as long as it might have taken Judy to count ten. It was as though the name Southcroft had turned the little woman to stone.

Then the hands came down slowly, and Mrs. Baxter waddled back to the tea table. She did not look at Judy; her face was expressionless.

"Have a piece of toast?" she said to Judy.

Judy took one. "Mrs. Baxter, I've come to ask you about Southcroft."

"Don't forget your milk, dear."

"No, I won't. Mrs. Baxter, I must ask you several things —"

"Just a minute, dear."

"Yes?"

"Perhaps you take jelly on your toast?"

"Yes, I do, but it doesn't matter. I'd rather you'd let me ask you —"

"But it does matter," said Mrs. Baxter firmly. "And I shall get the jelly for you. I don't use it myself, you know."

Judy had had dreams when she had tried to do something and could not because things — the same things — happened over and over again to prevent her. Now she watched Mrs. Baxter walk over to the shelves, watched the hands reach up to the jelly jar and — this time — bring it down and bring it back to the table. Judy sipped her milk and took another piece of toast. She was trying to steady herself for what she now realized was going to be very, very difficult. Mrs. Baxter had begun telling her about mountain climbing in the Alps. Her

voice went on and on, until Judy thought it would wear itself out.

The voice paused.

Judy said swiftly, "Tell me about Southcroft, please. What was it like to live in when you were there? Why is it so awful now?"

"No, dear," said Mrs. Baxter hurriedly. "I'd rather go on telling you about the Matterhorn."

"I want to know about Southcroft," cried Judy.

"No," said Mrs. Baxter. "I never talk about it. Never. I'll go on about the Matterhorn."

"Please. You must tell me about Southcroft." Judy was insisting, but she knew she was being beaten by the soft, little old woman. She found she was beginning to cry. "Please, Mrs. Baxter. My dad's ill with living there."

"Oh, no," cried the little woman. "Oh, no. he couldn't be!"

"He is," said Judy, "and you won't help!" Awkwardly, she began to get up.

"Won't you stay, dear, and hear about the Matterhorn?"

"No!" Judy tried to put her glass back on the dainty table, but couldn't see properly for her tears. The glass fell and broke as she turned from the table. She found the handle of the door and let herself out.

Judy ran down the long hallways. When she got outside, she ran and ran, and then walked and walked. She knew she could have caught a bus home, but she didn't

want to. She walked all the way, arriving at dusk, to find her mother waiting anxiously for her. But, instead of questioning Judy at once, Mrs. Cook drew her into the kitchen, where they were alone.

Mrs. Cook said, "Your dad telephoned from Walchester. He said he wasn't feeling very well, so he's spending the night with your Aunt Edie."

They stared at each other. Mr. Cook got along poorly with his sister Edie. "He'd do anything rather than come here," said Judy. "He's afraid."

Mrs. Cook nodded.

"Mom, we'll just have to move from here, for Dad's sake."

"I don't know that we can, Judy. Selling one house and buying another is very expensive; moving is expensive."

"But if we stay here . . . "

Mrs. Cook hesitated, and then asked, "Judy, what you were doing this afternoon — your calling on old Mrs. Baxter — was it any use, any help?"

"No."

Mrs. Cook groaned aloud.

Judy's visit to Mrs. Baxter had not answered any questions, but there was an outcome.

The next day, in the afternoon, Judy and Mike had come home from school and were in the kitchen with their mother. They were gloomy. There was no doubt at all that their father would come home this time — after all, here were his wife and his children that he loved — but the homecoming seemed likely to be a sad one.

From the kitchen, they heard the click of the front gate. This was far too early to be Mr. Cook himself, and, besides, there had been no sound of a car. Mike looked out the window. "No one we know," he reported. "An old lady."

Judy ran to open the front door before Mrs. Baxter had time to ring the bell. She brought her in and introduced her to the others. Besides her handbag, Mrs. Baxter was carrying a zip-up bag that seemed heavy; she kept it next to her. She was tired. "Buses!" she murmured.

They all sat around Mrs. Baxter, trying not to stare at her, waiting for her to speak.

"Your husband's not very well, I hear," she said at last to Mrs. Cook.

"No."

"Not home from work yet?"

"Not yet."

Mrs. Baxter was obviously relieved. She looked at them all now. "And this is the rest of the family. . . ." She smiled timidly at Mike: "You're the baby of the family?"

Mike said, "I'm younger than Judy. Mom, if it's okay, I think I'll go out on my bike with Charlie." He took something to eat and went out.

Mrs. Baxter said, "We never had children."

"A pity," said Mrs. Cook.

"Yes. Everything would be different, if it had been different." Mrs. Baxter paused. "Do you know, I've never been back to this house — not even to the village — since Mr. Baxter died."

"It was very sad for you," said Mrs. Cook, not knowing what else to say.

"It's been a terrible *worry* ," said Mrs. Baxter, as though sadness was not the thing that mattered. Again she paused. Judy could see that she was getting ready to say something important. She had been brave just to come all this way at all.

Mrs. Cook could also see what Judy saw. "You must be tired out," she said.

But Judy said gently, "Why have you come?"

Mrs. Baxter tried to speak, but couldn't. Instead she opened the zip-up bag and dragged out of it a large, heavy book: *The Vegetable and Fruit Grower's Encyclopedia and Vade-Mecum*. She pushed it into Mrs. Cook's lap. "It was Mr. Baxter's," she said. "Give it to your husband. Tell him to use it and work hard in the garden, and I think things will right themselves in time. You need to humor him."

Mrs. Cook was bewildered. She seized upon the last remark: "I humor him as much as I can, as it is. He's been so ill."

Mrs. Baxter giggled. "Good gracious, I didn't mean *your* husband. I meant mine. Humor Mr. Baxter."

"But — but he's dead and gone!"

Mrs. Baxter's eyes filled with tears. "That's just it; he isn't. Not both. He's dead, but not gone. He never meant to go. I knew what he intended. I knew the wickedness of it. I told him — I begged him on his deathbed, but he wouldn't listen. You know that saying: 'We brought nothing into this world, and it is certain that we can carry nothing out'? Well, there was something he'd dearly have liked to have taken out; he couldn't, so he stayed in this world with it: his garden." She wept noisily.

"Oh, dear, Mrs. Baxter!" said Mrs. Cook, much distressed.

"When he was dying," said Mrs. Baxter, after she had blown her nose, "I could see there was something he wanted to say. I leaned over him, and he managed to whisper his very last words. He said, 'Are the beans up yet?' Then he died."

Nobody spoke. Mrs. Baxter recovered herself and went on.

"I knew — I *knew* he wouldn't leave that garden after he'd died. I just hoped the next owners would look after it as lovingly as he'd done, and then in time he'd be content to go. That's what I hoped and prayed. But the first group of people were going to cover it with dog kennels, and I heard that the second lot were going to landscape it with artificial streams and weeping willows and things. Well, he made their lives a misery. And they left. And now your husband . . ."

"He just never liked gardening," said Mrs. Cook.

The two women stared at each other bleakly.

"Why can't Dad be allowed to watch television?" asked Judy. Then, answering herself: "Oh, I see: he ought to be working in the garden every spare minute in daylight and fine weather."

There was a long silence.

"It's good soil," said Mrs. Baxter. "Easy to work. Grows anything. That's why we came to live here, really. All my married life, I never had to buy a single vegetable. Fruit, too — raspberries, strawberries. So much of everything, for just the two of us, that we had to give a lot of stuff away. All those vegetables and fruits — you'd find it a great saving, with a family."

"It seems hard on my husband," said Mrs. Cook.

"It's hard on mine," said Mrs. Baxter. "Look at him!" Startled, Mrs. Cook and Judy looked where Mrs. Baxter was looking, through the French windows and down the length of the garden. The sun fell on the weedy earth of the garden and on nothing else.

Mrs. Cook turned her gaze back into the room, but Judy went on looking, staring until her eyes blurred and her vision was fogged with a kind of brown fogginess that was in the garden. Then, suddenly, she was afraid.

"But *look* !" said Mrs. Baxter, and took Judy's hand in her own. "*Look!*" Judy looked where she pointed, and the brown fogginess seemed to shape itself, and there, dimly, was the shape of an old man dressed in brown from his brown boots to his battered brown hat, with a piece of string tied around the middle of the old brown coat he was wearing. He stood in an attitude of dejection at the bottom of the garden, looking at the weeds.

Then Mrs. Baxter let go of Judy's hand,

and Judy saw him no more.

"That was his gardening coat," said Mrs. Baxter. "He insisted on wearing it. When all the buttonholes had gone, as well as the buttons, and I wouldn't repair it anymore, then he belted it with a string."

"He looked so miserable," said Judy. She had been feeling sorry for her father; now she began to feel sorry for Mr. Baxter.

"Yes," said Mrs. Baxter. "He'd like to go, I've no doubt of it, but he can't leave the garden in that state." She sighed. She gathered up her handbag and the other empty bag.

"Don't go!" cried Mrs. Cook and Judy together.

"What more can I do? I've told you; I've advised you. For *his* sake, too, I've begged

you. No, I can't do more."

She would not stay. She waddled out of the house and down the front path, and at the front gate met Mr. Cook. He had just gotten out of the car. She gave him a scared little nod, and scuttled away past him.

Mr. Cook came in wearily; his face was grayish. "Who was that old lady?" he asked. But he did not really want to know.

His wife said to him, "Arthur, I have a lot of things to explain. Come and sit down and listen."

Mrs. Cook talked and Mr. Cook listened, and gradually his face began to change. Something lifted from it, leaving it clear, almost happy, for the first time in weeks. At the end of Mrs. Cook's explanation, Judy added hers. She told her father what —

whom — she had seen in the garden, when Mrs. Baxter had held her hand. Mr. Cook began to laugh. "You saw him, Judy? An old man all in brown with a piece of string tied around his middle — oh, Judy, my girl! When I began really seeing him, only the other day, I was sure I was going off my rocker! I was scared! I thought I was seeing things that no one else could see — things that weren't there at all! And you've seen him, too, and he's just old man Baxter!" And Mr. Cook laughed so much that he cried, and in the end he put his head down and sobbed and sobbed.

It was going to be all right, after all.

In Mr. Baxter's old-fashioned mind, the man of the family was the one to do all the gardening. That was why, in what Judy considered a very unfair way, he had singled out her father. But now Mr. Cook's family rallied to him. Even Mike, when the need was explained, left his bicycle for a while. They all helped in the garden. They dug and weeded and planted seeds. Mr. Cook followed the advice of the *Encyclopedia* , and sometimes had excellent ideas of his own. When Judy asked him where he got them, he looked puzzled and said he did not know. But she could guess.

Every spare moment of daylight, Mr. Cook worked in the garden. His illness was cured. His appetite came back, and he slept like a top. He would have enjoyed television again, except that, in the middle of programs, he often fell asleep from healthy exhaustion.

More than a year later, on a trip to Walchester, Judy was passing a movie theater. An audience was just coming out from an afternoon showing. Judy felt a touch on her arm, soft yet insistent, like the voice that spoke—Mrs. Baxter's voice— "My dear, how — how is he?"

"Oh, Mrs. Baxter, he's much, much better! Oh, thank you! He's really all right. My mom says my dad's as well as she's ever known him."

"No, dear, I didn't mean your father. How is *he* — Mr. Baxter?"

Judy said, "We think he's gone. Dad hasn't seen the foggiest wisp of him for months, and Dad says it doesn't *feel* as if he's there anymore. You see, Dad's got the garden going wonderfully now. We've had early potatoes and beans and peas — oh, and raspberries — and Dad plans to grow asparagus —"

"Ah," said Mrs. Baxter. "No wonder Mr. Baxter's gone. Gone off pleased, no doubt. That *is* nice. I don't think you need worry about his coming back. He has enough sense not to. It won't be long before your father can safely give up gardening, if he likes."

"I'll tell him what you said," Judy replied doubtfully.

But, of course, it was too late. Once a gardener, always a gardener. "I'll never give up now," Mr. Cook said. "I'll be a gardener until my dying day."

"But not after that, Arthur," said his wife. "Please." ◆

READING CHECK

Answer the following questions about "The Strange Illness of Mr. Arthur Cook." You may want to check your answers by reviewing details in the story.

1. What condition was the garden in when the Cook family bought their new house? What did Mr. Cook say he might do in the garden?

2. Who were the two families who lived in the house before the Cooks bought it? What made Judy curious about the families?

3. What was the first sign of Mr. Cook's illness? What did he do that seemed to make him feel better for a while? What happened to Mr. Cook during his week of vacation?

4. What happened when Judy tried to ask Mrs. Cribble about the house? How did Mr. Biley treat her when she went to his office?

5. What did Judy tell Mrs. Baxter that seemed to shock the old woman? What did Mrs. Baxter leave for Mr. Cook on her visit to his house, and what advice did she have for him?

6. Who did Mrs. Baxter see in the garden? Why did she say that person was there?

7. How was Mr. Cook's strange illness cured?

WHAT DO YOU THINK

1. How would you describe Judy Cook as a character in the story?

2. How might the story have ended if Judy Cook had not gone to visit Mrs. Baxter?

3. Do you think that people who once lived in a house can leave their "spirits" behind? Explain your answer.

VOCABULARY CHECK

Read the following sentences and choose the correct meaning of each word in **bold print.** Then write each word and its meaning on your paper.

1. The Cooks could see that the other owners of the house had **neglected** the garden.
    (watered every day, left without care)

2. The house no longer looked **bleak** after the Cooks had lived there for a while.
    (gloomy, comfortable)

3. Mr. Biley thought Judy's questions about the house were **tiresome.**
    (interesting, annoying)

4. Judy was **insistent** about finding a reason for her father's illness.
    (determined, worried)

5. The Cooks were glad that Judy's **inquisitive** nature had brought an end to all of their troubles.
    (amazing, curious)

STRATEGY CHECK

The paragraph below is based on the story "The Strange Illness of Mr. Arthur Cook." Choose the correct word to fill in each blank. Use the rest of the paragraph and what you remember about the story to help you. Then write the whole paragraph on your paper.

   Mr. Cook was pleased when he bought a small house on a country r____. He planned to spend his free t____ watching television and relaxing. No one could explain the strange illness that came over him that spr____. His eyes blurred, he l____ his appetite, and couldn't fall asleep. It all seemed to have something to do with the g____. Before long, Mr. Cook was afraid even to come h____.

"POEMS ABOUT SOMETHING STRANGE"

These two poems have stories to tell. The first poem, "There was a Young Lady of Lynn," is a type of short, funny poem, called a limerick. "Sam" has a different kind of rhyme pattern, and it's longer so that the poet can create a feeling of mystery and suspense.

WORDS TO KNOW

The words in **bold print** are from "Poems About Something Strange." Study each word and its meaning carefully.

The Lady was **uncommonly** thin.

   uncommonly—unusually

When she **essayed** to drink the lemonade she did not succeed.

   essayed—tried, attempted

Sam liked to walk along the **shingle** and watch the sea.

   shingle—beach

On stormy nights, huge **billows** break on the shore.

   billows—waves

On calm nights the waves are **wallowing** peacefully in the moonlight.

   wallowing—rolling about

The **solitudinous** sea is so large and empty looking.

   solitudinous—lonely

THERE WAS A YOUNG LADY OF LYNN

ANONYMOUS

There was a young lady of Lynn,
Who was so uncommonly thin
   That when she essayed
   To drink lemonade,
She slipped through the straw and
  fell in.

SAM

by WALTER DE LA MARE

When Sam goes back in memory,
  It is to where the sea
Breaks on the shingle, emerald-green
  In white foam, endlessly;
He says—with small brown eye
  on mine—
  'I used to keep awake,
And lean from my window in the moon,
  Watching those billows break.
And half a million tiny hands,
  And eyes, like sparks of frost,
Would dance and come tumbling
  into the moon,
  On every breaker tossed.
And all across from star to star,
  I've seen the watery sea,
With not a single ship in sight,
  Just ocean there, and me;
And heard my father snore . . . And once,
    As sure as I'm alive,

Out of those wallowing, moon-flecked
  waves
  I saw a mermaid dive;
Head and shoulders above the wave,
  Plain as I now see you,
Combing her hair, now back, now front,
  Her two eyes peeping through;
Calling me, "Sam!"—quietlike—
  "Sam!" . . .
  But me . . . I never went,
Making believe I kind of thought
  'Twas someone else she meant . . .
Wonderful lovely there she sat,
  Singing the night away,
All in the solitudinous sea
  Of that there lonely bay.
P'raps,' and he'd smooth his hairless
  mouth,
  'P'raps, if 'twere *now,* my son,
P'raps, if I heard a voice say, "Sam!" . . .
  Morning would find me gone.'

WHAT DO YOU THINK?

1. Read "There Was a Young Lady of Lynn" aloud so that you can hear the sound pattern or rhyme and rhythm of this poem. The rhyme and rhythm of this poem is characteristic of all limericks. Which lines rhyme with each other? Imagine that the last line on the poem was changed to read "She slipped through the straw, quite dismayed." Would this poem still be a limerick? Explain why or why not.

2. Do you think the poet wants you to believe that Sam has been satisfied with his life? Explain why or why not.

3. Imagine Sam had told his story to a scientist who studied sea life. Do you think the scientist could explain Sam's experience of seeing and hearing a mermaid?

VOCABULARY CHECK

Read the following sentences and choose the correct meaning of each word in bold print. Then write each word and its meaning on your paper.

1. A woman thinner than a straw is **uncommonly** thin.
   (unusually, understandably)

2. The mermaid played among the **billows.**
   (pillows on a sofa, waves on the sea)

3. The beach at night was empty and **solitudinous.**
   (cold, lonely)

4. The moonlight glittered in the sea and the **shingle.**
   (beach, ships)

5. Sam **essayed** to get his friend to believe his odd story.
   (tried, wrote)

6. The waves were **wallowing** in the moonlight.
   (enormous, rolling about)

READING REVIEW

This unit is all about strange events that are often unexplained. Complete each sentence about a selection in the unit. Choose the best ending for each sentence. Then write the complete sentences on your paper.

1. In "The Willing," Robby became certain of his special power when ___ .
   a. the airplane was saved   c. the dogs ran away
   b. the car's tires blew out   d. the accidents stopped

2. Robby decided to will an accident into happening because he needed to ___ .
   a. prove he could prevent them   c. rescue a cat
   b. help his father   d. impress his teacher

3. In the article "The Cold Winds of Summer," the cold temperatures in the summer of 1816 were traced to ___ .
   a. a disease called cholera   c. dust from a volcano
   b. New England snowstorms   d. a terrible famine

4. In "Odd Things Happen," the main way that Robert Rickard seems to deal with strange events is to ___ .
   a. watch them happen   c. call the coast guard
   b. look into their causes   d. write them down

5. In "The Strange Illness of Mr. Arthur Cook," Judy questioned the old owners of her house because ___ .
   a. her father became ill there   c. the Cooks were lonely
   b. the roof was leaking   d. the garden had weeds

6. At the end of the story, Mr. Baxter was no longer seen outside the Cooks' house because the garden was ___ .
   a. in the sun   c. too much work
   b. full of weeds   d. well cared for

VOCABULARY REVIEW

Review some words that describe strange events from *Something Strange*.
Choose a word from the list to replace the words in **bold print** in each sentence
below. Then write the new sentences on your paper.

anxiously	**severe**	**mysteriously**
remarkable	**investigate**	**bewildered**

1. Sometimes it is best to **look into** strange stories so that the truth about them
   can be told.

2. Thousands of people died from a **very harsh** epidemic of cholera in the
   1800's.

3. Robby's friends were **puzzled** by his strange behavior.

4. The Cook family waited **in a worried way** for Mr. Cook's strange illness to
   disappear.

5. Mrs. Baxter told an **unusual** story about her husband's appearance in the
   garden.

6. Robert Rickard's reports show that odd things often fall **without
   explanation** from the sky.

WRITING ABOUT
SOMETHING STRANGE

1. Choose one of the strange events described in this unit that seemed the
   strangest of all to you — Robby's power to prevent accidents, odd things
   falling from the sky, the cold summer of 1816, or Arthur Cook's strange
   illness. Write a paragraph explaining why you believe the event you chose is
   stranger than any of the others.

2. The two main characters in the fictional stories in this unit are Robby, in
   "The Willing," and Judy, in "The Strange Illness of Mr. Arthur Cook." Write
   a paragraph about each character. Explain what made each character
   interesting. Explain what you liked, or disliked about each one.

UNIT

·4·

IT'S ABOUT TIME

Often, time seems to go by all too quickly. Happy times, such as a month at summer camp, or an evening at a school dance can seem to be as short as an hour. At other times, even a few minutes can seem like a very long time. The selections you will read in this unit are all about the passing of time and how it affects the lives of people and animals.

In the story, "Lucky Break," a boy named Toby tries to make sure that he is *not* in the right place at the right time. That is the only way he can avoid a fight with the toughest boy in school. In "My Kind of Watch," Clarence Day tells about a real problem he faced as a boy. In those days, people used pocket watches rather than wristwatches, and Clarence was hoping to get a certain kind of pocket watch to help him solve a problem with time.

"Nature's Amazing Clocks" is an article that explains some things scientists have learned about the way animals are able to tell time.

The play "Just a Matter of Time" tells about what one girl learns about herself when she has to face the changes that time brings into her life. The two poems that end this unit, "Marie Lucille" and "There Isn't Time!" remind us that often time seems to pass all too quickly.

Although you can measure and plan time, you can only experience the passage of time. You cannot control it. The selections in this unit will show you that what is most important about time may be how you choose to spend the time you have.

UNDERSTANDING WORDS IN SENTENCES

Words that Show How People Move or Change Over Time. The people and animals that you will read about in *"It's About Time"* are all affected by time. Certain words in the selections will help you understand how a character acts, feels, or changes. Some of these words are in **bold print.** Write each word and its meaning on your paper.

1. When his mother warned him to hurry, Toby **sprinted** down the block.
   (ran quickly, walked carefully)

2. Clarence was often late because **dawdling** had become a bad habit.
   (forgetting the time, moving too slowly)

3. Clarence did not like being late and he wanted to **reform.**
   (find an excuse, change bad behavior)

4. The thought of owning his own watch **spurred** Clarence on to try harder.
   (encouraged, surprised)

5. Scientists have learned a great deal about animal behavior by **observing** animals in the wild.
   (watching, operating)

6. Lisl found that she had to learn to **cope** with a difficult situation.
   (deal with, avoid)

◆ INTRODUCING ◆

"LUCKY BREAK"

Toby Fancher has a problem. Can he get through the whole day without Hulk Horgan getting to him? It's a question of timing — all Toby needs is a lucky break.

WORDS TO KNOW

The words in **bold print** are from "Lucky Break." Study each word and its meaning carefully.

Hulk headed toward Toby with long **strides.**
  strides — big, energetic steps

The gym teacher kept **darting** around the crowd.
  darting — quickly moving in and out

The teacher was **shepherding** the students back to class.
  shepherding — leading, moving along

Mr. Kelson **snickered** at his own joke.
  snickered — laughed in a slightly nasty way

The school did not **condone** violence.
  condone — agree with and accept

LUCKY BREAK

by ADRIENNE POPPER

The morning dawned hot and humid. When my alarm rang, I lay on my bed watching tiny pieces of dust swirl in the beam of light that slanted into the room through the slats of the blind. Yesterday, I had stood up to the terrible Hulk Horgan. That's why Hulk would be waiting for me today. I'm not much of a fighter, and Hulk would deck me with one punch. I rolled over, sat up, put my feet on the floor, and stared at my toes. There wasn't much point in hurrying to get dressed. Who ever rushed to his own execution?

I could hear the water running in the bathroom where my sister Abby was washing up, and the snap of the sheets as my mother made the bed in her room. Then my mother knocked on the door of my room. "Move it, Toby, it's almost 7:30." The stairs creaked at each step as she headed for the kitchen.

I didn't move. The later I got to school,

the safer I'd be. Hulk had a short temper—but he also had a short memory. By tomorrow Hulk would probably forget our argument. The problem was how to live through a whole day at school without running into Hulk—and having his fists run into my face. At least if I timed my arrival to the bell, Hulk wouldn't be able to attack me until school ended.

Every few minutes I'd hear my mother holler, "Hurry up, Toby Fancher" or, "You'll be late, Toby," but I continued to move in slow motion.

Abby was already walking out the door when I finally reached the kitchen. I sat at the table and chewed each bite of toast 12 times before I swallowed, to make breakfast last longer. My mother had stopped urging me to hurry and was taking out the flour and sugar and pans she needed to start the day's baking. She pretended to ignore me, but she kept glancing at my plate. She kept her lips pressed together in a thin line, as if words that she didn't want to escape would fly out if she relaxed her grip on them.

"Don't worry, Mom, I'll make it in time." I made a big show of grabbing my books and running out the door as if I were racing the bell. I sprinted the whole length of the block in case she decided to look out the front window and check my progress. Then, when I passed the bushes at the Petersens' house, where I knew my mother couldn't see me any longer, I slowed down. A baby could have crawled to school faster than I was walking.

I should have dawdled longer. When I reached the corner of Revere Street, I could see that the schoolyard was still full of kids. Even from a distance I could pick out Hulk, he was so much bigger than everyone else.

I scanned the knots of kids for Ronnie and Jeff, but before I could find them, Hulk found me. With long strides that became a run, he headed toward me. Anxious for some excitement, the other kids followed. They fanned out in a wedge behind him, a spearhead with Hulk at the point.

I threw my books into his path as he reached me and he stopped short.

"Hiiiyah! Ffft! Ffft! Yeeah!" I yelled as I waved my arms and kicked my right leg up high the way I had seen a karate black belt do on a show on TV. "Don't touch me; these fists are deadly." I kept hopping about, kicking out an arm and then a leg to keep Hulk at a distance. "I know karate, kung fu, jujitsu, szechuan . . . and a few other Japanese words, too," I shouted. The black

belt on TV had explained that loud noises unnerve your opponent.

Hulk didn't look unnerved. He looked puzzled, like a cat I had once seen watching a cicada flap and buzz and twist to free himself of his shell.

By this time, the other kids had formed a circle around us as we faced each other across my scattered books. I was still jumping around, throwing punches and kicks. But I was using up all my strength just to keep moving.

"He's gone crazy from the heat," someone shouted. "Yeah, he's loco," laughed another kid. They started making weird noises and imitating my karate punches and kicks at each other.

"You're dead, Fancher," Hulk said, and he stepped on my notebook to get to me.

"What's going on here? Horgan, hold it right there." Mr. Abruzzo, the gym teacher, was pushing past the last row of kids to get to us. The bell sounded. "All of you, get inside. Break it up now." Slowly, the crowd turned for the doors. "You, too, Horgan," he said, standing so close to Hulk that Hulk had no choice but to move toward the school. "And Fancher," he called out over his shoulder, "you're wanted in the office. Mr. Kelson wants to see you."

Mr. Abruzzo kept darting here and there behind Hulk and the crowd like a collie herding cows. I stayed right behind him until we were in the building and up the short flight of stairs to the first floor. Then I ran the rest of the way to Mr. Kelson's office.

I had to go into the school's main office to get to Mr. Kelson's. Entering the office was like walking into a meat locker. A blast of cool air and the screams from the school's two secretaries reached me at about the same moment.

"Hurry up in! Close the door!" they shouted in a chorus. The office was the only room in the school that had air conditioning, and the two women didn't want any of their comfort to leak out into the hall where the students could get some of it.

I stood at the partition that separated the secretaries' desks from a waiting area that contained two uncomfortable chairs, rows of mailboxes for the teachers, and a bulletin board with some notices pinned to it. Once the door was closed and the cold air locked safely inside, the secretaries ignored me and went on working at their desks. I tried clearing my throat. "Uhmm. Uhmm." No response. "Excuse me." Nothing.

I gave up trying to be polite. "Mr. Abruzzo said Mr. Kelson wanted to see me. I'm Toby Fancher," I said loudly. One of the two looked up, as if surprised that I was there.

"Have a seat," she said. "I'll tell Mr. Kelson you're here."

After a minute or so, the door to Mr. Kelson's office opened, and the secretary told me to go in. Mr. Kelson, the principal, was straightening papers at his desk.

There was an armchair opposite his desk, but he didn't ask me to sit down. "I have

a report from the school nurse that says you gave Thomas Horgan a bloody nose yesterday. Is that correct?"

I nodded. I bet Mr. Kelson was the only person in the whole world who would call Hulk "Thomas." I bet even Hulk's own mother never called him that. It made him sound human.

Mr. Kelson leaned across his desk and studied me more closely, as though he couldn't believe it. "You don't deny it?" I shook my head. "Well, well," he said, and he snickered a little. "Our very own David and Goliath."

I sort of smiled at that remark. This was definitely the wrong thing to do. He called back the snicker and set his face in a serious look. "Do you have any explanation?"

"No, sir." There was no point in explaining. If I told him that Hulk was teasing me, Mr. Kelson would suggest that I fight with words, not fists. Or he'd repeat that old sticks and stones poem about words not harming you. He's famous for that advice.

"We don't condone violence around here, Toby. If you must fight, I suggest that you do it with words, not fists. You're suspended from classes for today. You can spend your time in the office." He opened the door and waved an arm in the direction of the two uncomfortable chairs. "Toby will be staying in the office for the rest of today . . . and for detention, too," he added as an afterthought. The secretaries just nodded and kept on working. "You'll have the

whole day to think about how to handle differences of opinion," he said.

I hadn't counted on detention, too. But when I thought about it, it seemed like a lucky break, with the air conditioning and all. Besides, Hulk wouldn't hang around the school all the way through detention on a hot Friday afternoon, so my life might be safe all the way through the weekend.

I sat down in one of the uncomfortable chairs and put my books and my lunch bag on the other one. Mr. Kelson was right about having plenty of time to think. But I didn't plan to think about not fighting. I took out a piece of paper and began to figure how much a bike and all the accessories would cost me.

I spent the rest of the day, right through detention, dreaming about being able to go into town to buy a new bicycle. Finally, the very last bell of the week rang and I was free. ◆

READING CHECK

Answer the following questions about "Lucky Break." You may want to check your answers by reviewing details from the story.

1. Why did Toby want to arrive at school exactly when the bell rang?

2. What did Toby think Hulk would do to him when he met him in the schoolyard?

3. How did Hulk react when Toby pretended to use karate? How did the other kids in the schoolyard react?

4. What did Mr. Abruzzo tell Toby? How did Toby feel about this?

5. How did Toby explain why he had punched Hulk?

6. What did Mr. Kelson do to punish Toby?

7. How did Toby spend the rest of the school day?

WHAT DO YOU THINK?

1. Do you think that Toby's mother or Mr. Kelson could have helped him, if he had told either one of them the whole story? Explain why or why not.

2. Why did Toby pretend to know karate? What would you have done in his place?

3. What do you think will happen the next time Toby meets Hulk? Use details from the story to explain your answer.

VOCABULARY CHECK

Read the following sentences and choose the correct meaning of each word in **bold print.** Then write each word and its meaning on your paper.

1. Toby kept **darting** around the school yard, pretending to be doing karate.
   (jumping up and down, moving quickly in and out)

2. The other boys **snickered** when they heard what Toby told Hulk.
   (laughed, sighed)

3. The principal would not **condone** fighting.
   (consider, accept)

4. When the bell rang, the teacher began **shepherding** the students into school.
   (leading, sneaking)

5. Toby took long **strides** toward the principal's office.
   (big steps, big excuses)

STRATEGY CHECK

The paragraph below is based on the story "Lucky Break." Choose a word that makes sense to fill in each blank. Use the rest of the paragraph and your knowledge of the story to help you.

Toby thought that the later he got to sch____, the safer he'd be. His mother told him to h____, but he moved as slowly as he could. In the schoolyard, kids gathered around to see Hulk and Toby f____. Hulk wasn't worried when Toby said he knew k____. In the end, Toby was glad he had to spend the day in the principal's o____.

"MY KIND OF WATCH"

Clarence's father thinks that it is important that he be on time for everything, but somehow Clarence is always late. That means that Clarence often gets into trouble. Perhaps a watch would help? Well it might — if it is the right kind of watch. Read this true story to find out how Clarence's problem gets solved.

WORDS TO KNOW

The words in **bold print** are from "My Kind of Watch." Study each word and its meaning carefully.

George was the most **reliable** child in the family because he was always on time for breakfast.
> **reliable** — dependable, able to count upon

Father insisted that Clarence learn to be **prompt.**
> **prompt** — on time

The watch had a hard case made of **nickel.**
> **nickel** — a hard metal

Because the watch kept breaking, Clarence was convinced it was not **practicable.**
> **practicable** — practical, useful

Clarence did not appreciate **heirlooms.**
> **heirlooms** — things passed down from generation to generation

The watch **crystal** broke whenever Clarence got into a fight.
> **crystal** — glass cover on the face of a watch

MY KIND OF WATCH

by CLARENCE DAY

Father always made a great point of our getting down to breakfast on time. I meant to be prompt. But it never occurred to me that I had better try to be early. My idea was to slide into the room at the last moment. Therefore, I was often late.

My brothers were often late, too, except for George. He was the only really reliable son Father had. George got down so early, Father pointed out to me, that he even had time to practice a few minutes on the piano.

The reason George was so prompt was that he was in a hurry to see the sports pages before Father got hold of the newspaper. The reason he played the piano was to send signals to the rest of us, as we got dressed upstairs. George had made up a code to tell us which team had won the baseball game. When he played a happy, lively tune, it meant the Giants had won. A sad tune meant the Reds had beaten the Giants.

The fact remained that George was always on time. Father was so pleased by George's promptness that he bought a pocket watch for him and had it engraved on the back. It said: *George Parmly Day, Always on time.* Father told me that, since I was the oldest, he had meant to give me a watch first, and he showed me the one he had bought for me. It was just like George's, except that nothing had been engraved on it yet. Father explained that he would have to put it away for a while, until I had earned it by getting down early to breakfast.

Time went on, without much improvement on my part. Dawdling had gotten to be a habit with me. Sometimes my lateness was serious. One morning, when breakfast was half over and I had nothing on but my underwear, Father called up from the front hall that I was to come down that instant. When I shouted indignantly that I wasn't dressed yet, he said he didn't care. "Come down just as you are, confound it!" he roared. I was tempted to take him at his word, but I thought there might be some catch in it and didn't; still, I hurried all I could.

Father ate his usual hearty breakfast in a stormy mood. I ate my usual hearty breakfast, too. But I felt guilty and nervous. No matter what, we always ate heartily. I sometimes wished afterward that I hadn't, but Father's mood never seemed to hurt him.

Mother told Father that if he would give me the watch, she was sure I'd do better. He said that he didn't believe it, and that that was a poor way to bring a boy up. To prove to him that he was wrong, Mother gave me

a watch that had belonged to one of her elderly cousins. It was really too valuable a watch for a boy to wear, she said. She warned me to be very careful with it. I promised I would.

This watch, however, turned out to be painfully delicate. It was old, I was young. We were not exactly made for each other. It had a case of thin gold. Since Mother had had the former owner's monogram shaved off the front cover, that cover used to sink in the middle when pressed. Also, the lid fit so closely that there was barely room for the glass crystal over the face of the watch. Such a very thin crystal had to be used that any pressure on the lid broke it.

I didn't press on the lid, naturally, after the first time this happened. I was careful, and everything would have gone well if other boys had been careful, too. But it was not practical for me to make them be careful. When I had a fight, friendly or otherwise, I used to ask my opponent if he would be so kind as not to punch me on the left side of my stomach near the pocket where I kept the watch. He might or might not listen. If he and I were too excited and kept on long enough, the watch crystal broke, anyway. There was never time to take out my watch first, and anyhow, there was no place to put it. A watch that goes around in a boy's pocket has to take life as it comes. This watch had never been designed for such a fate.

The first two crystals I broke, Mother paid for. Father disapproved of the whole

business and would have nothing to do with it. But I hated to trouble Mother — and she hated to be troubled, too. "Oh, Clarence, dear! You haven't broken your watch again?" she cried when I opened the cover the second time, to show her the shattered fragments. She was so upset, that I felt too guilty to tell her the next time it happened.

From then on, I had to pay for the damage myself.

My pocket money never amounted to very much. Every new crystal cost one quarter of my allowance. It was a serious drain.

Wrestling and rolling around on the floor with Sam Willets, I forgot about my watch until — I would suddenly hear a faint tinkle. I would pick out the broken glass and leave the watch with no crystal until I had enough money on hand, but these delays made me nervous. I knew that Mother wanted to feel sure I was taking good care of the watch. She might look at it any evening. As soon as I had the money, I hurried over to a tiny watch shop and left it there to be fixed. When I got there late, the two old men who owned the shop made me leave the watch overnight. I didn't have one easy moment until I got it back the next day.

I gave up at last. I told Mother I didn't want to wear the watch anymore.

Then I found, to my amazement, that this way out of my troubles was barred. The watch was an heirloom. And an heirloom was a thing that its owner must cherish. No good child, I was told, should fail to appreciate heirlooms.

I left Mother's room in low spirits. That night, as I wound up my watch, I envied George. Father had selected the right kind of watch for George; he knew what a boy needed. It had a thick nickel case and an almost unbreakable crystal. And it got through the day without problems, even when dropped in the bathtub.

It seemed to me that I was facing a pretty dark future. For months I had had no money to buy anything else. In some way that I didn't fully understand, I was tied to a watch I now hated — a delicate thing that would always make trouble unless I learned to live more carefully.

Then I saw a way out. All this time I had kept on being late for breakfast at least once a week, out of habit. Now it occurred to me that if I could reform, perhaps Father might give in and give me that reliable nickel watch he had bought. I reformed. Sometimes I weakened, but every time that crystal got broken, I was spurred on to fresh efforts. When I had finally set a record for promptness that satisfied Father, he had my name engraved on the watch he had bought, and presented it to me. He was a little surprised at the great pleasure I showed on this occasion. As he watched me hopping around the room in delight, he said. "Don't be so excited, confound it." "You'll knock over that vase."

Mother said she couldn't see why Father should give me a nickel watch when I had a gold one already. He just laughed and told her that "that old thing" was no kind of a watch for a boy. So, reluctantly, she put it away again in her jewel box.

Her parting shot at Father was that anyhow she had been right. She had said all along that a watch was what I needed to teach me how to be prompt. ◆

READING CHECK

Answer the following questions about "My Kind of Watch." You may want to check your answers by reviewing details from the story.

1. Why was Clarence often late for breakfast? Why was George always on time?

2. When did Father say Clarence would recieve a watch with his name engraved on it?

3. Why did Mother give Clarence a watch that had belonged to an old relative? How did Clarence feel about this gift?

4. What did Clarence end up spending his pocket money on? Why was this necessary?

5. How did Mother react when Clarence tried to return her gift to her? How did this make Clarence feel?

6. Why did Clarence start showing up on time for breakfast?

7. What did Father give Clarence as a reward for his being on time? How did Clarence react when he received this gift?

WHAT DO YOU THINK?

1. Do you think that Father was right to make Clarence earn the watch in the way that he did? Explain why or why not.

2. Why was Mother correct in saying that a watch was what Clarence needed to teach him to be on time?

3. Do you think that being on time is very important? Explain why or why not.

VOCABULARY CHECK

Read the following sentences and choose the correct meaning for each word in **bold print.** Then write each word and its meaning on your paper.

1. Father wanted to teach Clarence to be **prompt.**
   (on time, careful)

2. Clarence spent money on many new watch **crystals.**
   (gold chains, glass covers)

3. Mother's jewelry box contained several **heirlooms.**
   (time pieces, old family things)

4. The delicate watch was not a **practicable** gift.
   (perfect, useful)

5. George's watch was more **reliable.**
   (realistic, dependable)

6. The **nickel** watch was the one he wanted.
   (hard metal, cheap toy)

STRATEGY CHECK

The paragraph below is based on the story "My Kind of Watch." Choose a word that makes sense to fill in each blank. Use the rest of the paragraph and your knowledge of the story to help you. Then write the whole paragraph on your paper.

Father made a point of everyone getting to br____ on time. Clarence and his brothers were often l____. His father promised him a w____ when he learned to arrive on time. Mother gave Clarence an old watch that br____ very often. Finally Clarence showed up on time because it was the only way he would ever be able to wear a watch that he would not have to spend all his m____ fixing.

"NATURE'S AMAZING CLOCKS"

You may have to set your alarm clock to make sure that you get up at the right time in the morning. But many animals have their own mysterious ways of telling time. Read this article to find out about some of the things different animals can do and the work scientists are doing to try to find out about these animals' abilities.

WORDS TO KNOW

The words in **bold print** are from "Nature's Amazing Clocks." Study each word and its meaning carefully.

Because the rooster crows every morning, it is hard to **ignore.**
   ignore — not notice

The scientists were interested in learning more about the **biological** patterns that animals use to tell time.
   biological — having to do with the science of living things.

The white fur of the snowshoe rabbit is a perfect **camouflage** in snowy weather.
   camouflage — coloring that blends in with background and protects animal from being seen

The bees collected the **nectar** from the flowers in the field.
   nectar — sweet juice from plants collected by bees to make honey

NATURE'S AMAZING CLOCKS

by MARILYN BURNS

The world runs on many different well-timed rhythms. These rhythms are regular cycles of change. Living things have always had to keep in time with the earth's changes in order to survive.

All living things have their own biological rhythms to help them exist in the world. These rhythms are their timekeeping methods. They're so powerful and so mysterious that they've fascinated people for a long, long time.

What are these rhythms in living things? Where do they come from? How are these inner clocks tuned to the rest of the world?

Telling Time Without Clocks

Roosters get up early every day. They insist on announcing this, too, with their crowing. That daily cycle is hard to ignore if you've got a rooster for a neighbor. If you wanted to be sure to get up at sunrise every day, chances are that you would need an alarm clock. But roosters have their own "clock" — inside.

Australian flying foxes are nocturnal fruit bats. They spend their days sleeping upside-down in the leaves of trees. At dusk they're hungry, so they fly out to feed at nearby fruit plantations. Australians who work on the plantations say that they always know when it is time to stop work each day. That's because the flying foxes arrive at exactly the same time every afternoon. If it weren't for these timely bats, the workers would have to depend on their watches.

Every year, swallows fly from their winter home in South America to the mission at San Juan Capistrano in California. People often go there to see them arrive. It's easy to plan the time to go, because the swallows come on about March 19 every year. They do that without the help of a calendar.

The pileated tinamou is a bird that lives in Panama. It looks like a tiny ostrich. Most people who live there call it the "three-hour bird." (That's a lot easier to say than pileated tinamou.) Every three hours this bird sings, day and night. Some people in Panama believe you can set your watch by the song of the three-hour bird. Some have done checks with the airport clock and found that the birds are never more than a few minutes off. No one knows for sure how this bird's inner clock works.

The Big Question

Many scientists have made careful investigations with animals, trying to understand the secrets of biological rhythms. There's one big question that these scientists have wondered about. The question is: are the natural rhythms in animals *external,* or are they *internal?*

External rhythms are brought about because of some outside force. Internal rhythms control the animal's behavior without being affected by outside forces.

Scientists have done many experiments to find out whether certain living things have internal or external rhythms. The reports that follow tell about some of the experiments scientists have done.

Winter Clocks

Snowshoe rabbits have been used for some experiments. The snowshoe rabbit grows a white winter coat for camouflage, or protection against being seen in the snow. Their coats all start changing in late summer. The change to white is complete by fall. How do these animals know when to start growing their winter coats so that the camouflage is ready for the first snowfall?

The scientists did some experiments to find out. They put snowshoe rabbits in a laboratory where they could be observed. They did this in early summer, long before the coats of the rabbits started to change. The scientists wanted to see if the rabbits could be made to change the color of their coats sooner than usual.

First they made the temperature in the laboratory colder, to see if lower temperature was what caused the rabbits to change color in winter. Nothing happened.

Then they wondered if light was the clue. The days start getting noticeably shorter in late summer. So the scientists blindfolded the rabbits for several hours each day to make it seem that the days were getting shorter more quickly. Sure enough, the rabbits' coats began to change from brown to white.

The scientists' conclusion was that the change in the amount of light brought about the change in color.

Bees' Built-In Clocks

Many people have noticed that bees are excellent timekeepers. Dr. Auguste Forel was the first to report this in 1906. Dr. Forel lived in Switzerland. In good weather, he liked to eat his breakfast on the terrace near his garden. His meal always included fresh jams and jellies.

Soon he noticed that he wasn't the only one who liked jams and jellies. Bees always seemed to be buzzing around, trying to get a taste. Dr. Forel ate breakfast at the same time every day, and the bees came on time, too.

Even though the bees were a bit of a nuisance, Dr. Forel got interested in their behavior. On mornings when he ate inside, he would check the terrace. Sure enough, the bees would be there. This puzzled him. How could the bees keep such good time? At first he had thought it was the aroma of the fruit in the jams that attracted them, but when he ate indoors, the bees could not smell his breakfast. How could they know what time to come when there was no jam or jelly out there? He had no answer.

A few years later, another scientist, Dr. Hugo von Buttel-Reepen, also noticed how bees kept time. He often took walks through buckwheat fields because he enjoyed the buckwheat flowers. They had a wonderful aroma. He got used to hearing the bees buzzing while they were collecting nectar from the blossoms.

He also noticed that in the middle of the morning, at about 10 o'clock, the bees would all leave. That was understandable to Dr. von Buttel-Reepen. He knew that the buckwheat flowers stopped their flow of nectar at about that time. The buckwheat flowers' inner clocks didn't interest him as much as the bees' inner rhythms did. How did they know exactly when to come to collect the nectar? They always seemed to be on time.

He guessed that the bees had an actual sense of time. But is this time sense something that bees have within them, or is it controlled by some force out in the world? In other words, was the rhythm internal or external? Other scientists would help to answer that question.

A Complete Clock Check

Karl von Frisch, a German scientist, studied the behavior of bees for many, many years. He wondered about the reports of their timekeeping, and in 1940 he designed an experiment to check on their inner clocks.

His idea was to train a group of bees to come for food at the same time every day, just as Dr. Forel had accidentally done with his jams and jellies. Then he would build a box to hold the bees and put them on a fast boat to the United States. Would they keep feeding at local German time? If so, that would show they had independent internal clocks. Or would they shift their feeding time as they crossed time zones? This would show that they responded to outside clues.

Karl von Frisch built the boxes for the bees. He hired a student to take the sea voyage with the bees and note what time they came to feed each day. Soon after, the student and the bees set sail for America.

Dr. von Frisch waited for the student to return with the reports. Unfortunately, not one single note had been made during the voyage. The student had been seasick the entire time and was never able to get out of bed!

It wasn't until 1955 that Dr. von Frisch designed another experiment. By then there were fast flights from Germany to the United States, so there was no danger of seasickness. He asked another scientist, Max Renner, to take charge of this experiment.

Two bee rooms were built for the experiment. One was put together in Paris, and the other in the Museum of Natural History in New York City. The rooms were eight feet by fifteen feet, and they were identical in every way.

In Paris, Max Renner trained 40 bees to come to a feeding dish at every day between 8:15 AM and 10:15 AM. When he decided they were all well trained, he packed them in a special box and flew with them to New York. When he got to New York, he raced to the museum. Less than 24 hours after he had left Paris, the bees were in the other identical room.

Renner wondered if the bees would continue to feed at Paris time or if they would change their schedules to feed at 9 AM New York time since New York was in a different time zone. He didn't have to wait long for the answer. The bees continued to feed at 9 AM Paris time. The first bees came out of their hive at 3:15 AM.

This was an exciting answer to the question that Dr. Forel had wondered about many years earlier. The conclusion was that bees do have internal clocks that seem to be unaffected by the outside world. This timing ability of bees seemed to be an example of an internal rhythm.

The Cycles of the Fiddler Crab

The fiddler crab is another well-timed creature. You can observe its time sense by noticing the color of its shell. In the daytime, the fiddler crab has a dark greenish-brown shell. In the nighttime, its shell is much lighter, a pale brown color. The change happens when spots of dark pigment in the shell start to cluster together about the time of sunrise. This change from light to dark happens on a regular daily schedule of exactly 24 hours.

Not only does the fiddler crab's color follow this 24-hour cycle daily, it pays attention to the tides as well. The time of day when the fiddler crab's color is the darkest is always when the tide is lowest. That's also when the crab is the most active, feeding on algae and other microorganisms left on the mud when the tide goes out. So the crab's dark shell at this time is a handy camouflage, protecting it from larger sea animals.

Low tide doesn't happen at the same time every day, though. Each day, low tide occurs about 50 minutes later than it did the day before. So, each day, the crab's shell will be at its darkest 50 minutes later than the day before.

Scientists have concluded that the fiddler crab has two kinds of inner clocks that work together. One is an external rhythm that is tuned to tidal changes. The other is a 24-hour daily internal rhythm. Observing the habits of fiddler crabs has produced important clues to the timekeeping abilities of all living things. ◆

READING CHECK

Answer the following questions about "Nature's Amazing Clocks." You may want to check your answers by reviewing details from the article.

1. What does an inner clock tell an animal?

2. What does the word "nocturnal" tell you about the habits of the Australian flying fox?

3. What do most people in Panama call a pileated tinamou? Why was the bird given this nickname?

4. When scientists did research on snowshoe rabbits what did they discover about the way light affects the color of the animals? What questions remained unanswered after the experiment?

5. What did Dr. von Frisch and his team hope to find out from their experiments with bees? What conclusions did they reach from their experiments?

6. What is an external rhythm? Name one animal described in this article that shows an example of an external rhythm.

7. What is an internal rhythm? Name one animal described in this article that shows an example of an internal rhythm.

WHAT DO YOU THINK?

1. Explain the meaning of the statement, "Living things have always had to keep in time with the earth's changes in order to survive."

2. Why do scientists conduct experiments? What other ways do they have of finding out about animal behavior?

3. Do you think that people sometimes do things according to an inner clock? Use examples from your own habits and those of people you know to explain your answer.

VOCABULARY CHECK

Read the following sentences and choose the correct meaning of each word in **bold print.** Then write each word and its meaning on your paper.

1. The bees liked the **nectar** from the buckwheat flowers.
   (blossoms, sweet juice)

2. Every creature follows its own **biological** rhythms.
   (having to do with the science of personality, having to do with the scientific study of life forms)

3. White fur is good **camouflage** in the snow.
   (protection from the cold, protection from being seen)

4. The man could not **ignore** the bees that gathered at breakfast.
   (not notice, not eat)

STRATEGY CHECK

The paragraph below is based on the article "Nature's Amazing Clocks." Choose a word that makes sense to fill in each blank. Use the the rest of the paragraph and your knowledge of the article to help you. Then write the whole paragraph on your paper.

All living things have their own inner rhythms that are methods of keeping t____. In Australia, flying foxes arrive at the plantations at the same time every d____. Dr. Hudson found that cows always seemed to know when it was Sunday, the day they got a salt-stick tr____. Scientists are very interested in whether an animal's inner cl____ is controlled by forces inside the animal or by outside forces. They often do e____ which they hope will help them answer many of their questions.

"JUST A MATTER OF TIME"

Lisl knew that she had to grow up sometime. She just thought that her mother would always be there to help her and guide her. In this moving play, Lisl must come to accept the fact that she won't have her mother around much longer. Read this play to find out what Lisl does when she discovers that important changes, both bad and good, can sometimes be just a matter of time.

WORDS TO KNOW

The words in **bold print** are from "Just A Matter of Time." Study each word and its meaning carefully.

A Revolutionary War soldier was buried in the **cemetery** near Lisl's house.
   cemetery — graveyard

The hospital **corridor** led to Jean's room.
   corridor — hallway

Jean was on the **faculty** of the college.
   faculty — teaching staff at a school

Although Jean was a successful woman, many times she felt **insecure** about decisions she had made.
   insecure — not sure or safe

JUST A MATTER OF TIME

a teleplay by PAUL W. COOPER

Cast of Characters

Lisl Gilbert, a high school senior
Jean Gilbert, Lisl's mother
Louis Gilbert, Lisl's father
Jane, Lisl's older sister
Jim, Jane's husband
Mrs. Canby, a social worker
Jo, Lisl's best friend
Jeff, another friend of Lisl's
Narrator 1
Narrator 2

Narrator 1: Lisl and Jo are walking past a cemetery on their way home from school.

Jo: I don't know why we came this way. This place gives me the creeps.

Lisl: Why? It's very peaceful here. Did you know that a soldier from the Revolutionary War is buried in there?

Jo: Really? How do you know?

Lisl: I come here with my mom when she does headstone rubbings.

Jo: Wow, your mom is into everything — painting, music, teaching art at the college. I wish my mom were talented and glamorous like yours.

(Lisl smiles proudly.)

Narrator 2: Later, Lisl arrives home. Her mother is there, working on a painting.

Lisl: Hi, Mom.

Jean: Hi, Lisl. Come and take a look. Does it need more green?

Lisl *(studying the painting)*: More blue, I think. *(She sits down.)* What are you doing home? I thought you had a meeting.

Jean *(working on her painting)*: Something came up.

Lisl: What time are Jim and Jane coming to visit this weekend?

Jean: They're not coming. *(She tries to sound cheerful.)* I'm afraid your dear old mom is checking into the hospital instead.

Lisl *(shocked)*: The hospital?

Jean: I saw the doctor this afternoon about that sore throat I've had. He found a little tumor on my lung. He insists on removing it right away.

Lisl: A tumor? Mom it isn't . . . cancer, is it?

Jean *(sitting next to her)*: Lisl, honey, would I be painting and talking like this if I thought it was cancer? I'm going in Saturday. The operation is Sunday morning. Now, do you think you could spend the weekend at Jo's house?

Lisl: Sure, I guess so.

Jean *(getting up)*: Good. Honey, I'm never going to finish this painting in time. Will you start dinner for me, please?

Lisl *(confused about her feelings)*: Sure, Mom.

Narrator 1: Lisl spends the weekend with Jo. On Sunday afternoon, she goes home, planning to visit the hospital with her father. When she gets home, the phone rings. Her sister, Jane, is calling from the hospital.

Jane: Lisl, Jim and I are at the hospital with Dad.

Lisl: You are? What are you doing in town? I thought—

Jane: Just listen to me, please. It's Mom. Something has happened. *(Lisl looks frightened.)* Can you get on a bus and come to the hospital?

Lisl: Yes. Sure. But, Jane, what is it?

Jane: Just come to the sixth floor of the hospital.

Narrator 2: In the hospital waiting room, Jane and her husband, Jim, sit together. Jane has been crying. Across the room her father, Louis, stares out a window.

Jim: How do you think your dad is taking it?

Jane: You know Dad. He's never been able to share his feelings. I think he's all right.

(Lisl enters.)

Lisl: She's going to die, isn't she?

(Her father turns to look at her, but he can't speak. Jane starts crying. Jim goes over to Lisl.)

Jim: The tumor was bad, Lisl. Cancer has spread through her lungs. It's only a matter of time now.

Louis *(coming over to them)*: I begged her to see the doctor months ago. She was always too busy.

(There is a long silence. Then Lisl speaks — without emotion.)

Lisl: How long has she got?

Jane: Two . . . maybe three months.

Lisl *(stunned)*: Months?

Jane: We'll still have some time with her. But first she'll have to recover from the operation.

Lisl *(angry)*: Recover? For what? So she can die? Why don't they let her die right now?

Jim *(holding her shoulder)*: Lisl —

Lisl: Why does she have to get better in order to die?

Jim: Because that's the way it is. The cancer isn't strong enough yet. It will get stronger and stronger, until . . .

(He stops without finishing the sentence. Lisl backs away. She turns and runs into the corridor. Jim runs after her. When he reaches her, she collapses in his arms, sobbing. Louis and Jane join them.)

Jim: Go ahead and cry, Lisl. Let it out. We're all going to need our strength for what's ahead.

Narrator 1: When they get home, Lisl stares at a painting over the fireplace. She remembers when her mother won a prize for it. And she remembers congratulating her mother afterwards.

Lisl's Voice: I'm proud of you, Mom.

Jean's Voice: Thank you, Lisl. Remember, always be original. Whenever you do something, make it special. *Be* someone special.

(Jane comes in and sees Lisl staring at the painting.)

Lisl: She's so special. She does everything well. *(She pauses.)* Jane, I'm nothing without her. What am I going to do?

171

Jane: You're going to cope. You're going to keep on living, just like the rest of us.

Lisl: But she's —

Jane: She's your mother, and you're somebody else. You are two different people. Don't live your life in Mom's shadow, Lisl.

Narrator 2: Two weeks later, Lisl is walking to school. Jeff pulls up on his motorbike.

Jeff: Hi, Lisl. Hop on, and I'll take you to school.

Lisl: No, thanks, Jeff.

Jeff: Hey, are you mad at me or something? You've been acting real strange lately.

Lisl: I guess I have a lot on my mind.

Jeff: How's your mom?

Lisl *(nervously)*: I keep telling you, she's fine. She'll be home in a few weeks, good as new.

Jeff: My sister is in one of her classes. She says everybody really misses her.

Lisl: That's nice. I'll tell her.

Jeff: Tell her hello for me, too.

Narrator 1: He drives off. Lisl stares into space. She remembers a family celebration when her mother became a college professor. Then she remembers watching her mother surrounded by students who admire her. In each scene, Lisl is proud of her mother. She is also worried that she will never measure up to her.

(Lisl visits her mother in the hospital. They walk slowly along a corridor as they talk.)

Lisl: Oh, and Jeff says hello. His sister told him the kids in your class miss you. And Jo asked if she could visit you.

Jean: I appreciate that, Lisl, but I'd rather she didn't. I must look awful.

Lisl: Oh, no, Mom. You don't. *(Jean's face suddenly shows pain.)* Mom, are you all right? Let's go back to your room.

Jean: No, please. I'm fine. I need the exercise so I can get strong enough to go home.

Lisl: All right. *(She smiles.)* We want you home an awful lot.

Jean: Really? Have you and Dad missed me?

(Lisl looks amazed at her mother's question, but does not answer.)

Narrator 2: Two weeks later, Lisl is in the kitchen. Jane comes in.

Jane: Lisl, we're waiting for you. Mrs. Canby has been here ten minutes.

Lisl *(angry)*: Why did you bring her here? Mom's been home only three days. The last thing we need is an outsider.

Jane: An outsider is exactly what we need. Someone has to help us face the truth about Mom. Mrs. Canby is a trained social worker. She knows what she's doing.

Narrator 1: Lisl joins the family in the living room. She looks coldly at Mrs. Canby.

Mrs. Canby: Jean, why don't we start with you? Will you share your feelings with us?

Jean: Well, I guess . . . I don't feel as though I'm dying.

(Lisl shudders at this last word. She stares at her mother.)

Jean: I feel as though I'm getting better. Maybe I won't die.

Mrs. Canby: What about you, Louis? What do you feel?

Louis *(after a long pause)*: I don't feel anything.

(He turns away, as if to hide what he really feels.)

Jane *(suddenly crying)*: I don't want her to die! It isn't fair! *(She sobs quietly.)*

Mrs. Canby: Lisl, look at your mother. Tell her what you see.

(Lisl stares angrily at Mrs. Canby. Then she looks at her mother, and her eyes fill with tears.)

Lisl *(softly)*: I see . . . a lovely . . . tired face. *(She begins to cry. Then she turns angrily to Mrs. Canby.)* Mrs. Canby, we appreciate your coming here, but we can manage fine on our own. I don't think we need anyone to tell us how to watch our mother die!

Narrator 2: Later, Lisl goes to Jo's house. Jo is in her room.

Jo: Hi. Come on in. My mother said she'd call the Department of Health if I didn't clean my closet. *(She notices Lisl's expression.)* Lisl, is something wrong?

Lisl: I've been lying to you, Jo. My mother isn't fine. She has cancer, and she's going to die.

Jo: Oh, no! Have you known that all this time? Why didn't you tell me? Lisl, how much time . . . does she . . . ?

Lisl: A couple of months, maybe.

(Jo is shocked. She puts her arms around Lisl and cries.)

Jo: Oh, Lisl, I'm so sorry.

Lisl *(bursting into tears)*: I'm going to be alone, Jo. I won't have her anymore, and I need her so much.

Jo *(wiping her eyes)*: Listen. If it means anything, you've always got me.

Narrator 1: That night, Lisl is eating dinner alone. Her father comes downstairs and sits down to eat.

Louis: She's asleep.

Lisl *(after a pause)*: Dad, can we talk? We haven't ever discussed what's happening to Mother.

(He looks at her, then back at his plate.)

Louis: I'm not in the mood for talking, Lisl.

Lisl: Dad, I know you still think of me as a kid, but I'm not. I'm old enough to talk about death. And it would really help if you'd let me.

(He looks at her, afraid to let his feelings show.)

Louis: You're right. You have grown up, and we do need to talk about it. It's just that . . . well . . . we'll talk later, all right? *(He gets up and leaves the room.)*

Narrator 2: The next day, Lisl goes to Mrs. Canby's office.

Mrs. Canby *(surprised but courteous)*: What brings you here, Lisl?

Lisl: Two things, I guess. First, I want to apologize for being rude. Second, I could use someone to talk to.

Mrs. Canby: First, no apology is necessary. And second, it's my job to be someone to talk to.

Lisl: I'm not sure where to start. This is turning my life upside-down. It's not only because my mother is dying. I feel as if I'm dying, too. I can't study. My dad won't talk to me. I feel like a great big zero.

Mrs. Canby: Can you tell me why?

Lisl: I've always been a nothing. I've never been special like my mom. She has everything to offer. I have nothing. Here I am strong and healthy, while she's dying. I feel that I should be the one who's dying.

Mrs. Canby: I see. Well, if you don't think you're very special, what are you going to do about it?

Lisl: I don't know. My only claim to fame is that I'm my mother's daughter. And no one can top her.

Mrs. Canby: Do you have to top her? You've spent a lot to time trying to measure up to her. Maybe you've failed to see what makes you special.

Lisl: Jane said something like that. But *is* there something special about me?

Mrs. Canby: It's up to you to find that out.

Narrator 1: When Lisl gets home, her mother is packing her art supplies into boxes.

Lisl: Mom, don't put those away. Use them.

Jean: There's no time. *(She holds up a prize ribbon.)* Do you know why they gave me this prize? My painting was the only realistic one in the show. *(She drops the ribbon into a wastebasket.)*

Lisl: That isn't true!

Jean: I'm afraid it is. And do you know why the college hired me as a professor?

There were plenty of men on the faculty, and they needed a woman. *(She pauses.)* I almost wish I hadn't gotten the job. It took up so much of my time. I was always so busy rushing around, trying to be successful.

Narrator 2: Later, Lisl writes in the journal she's been keeping. We hear her saying what she's writing.

Lisl's Voice: Today I met a part of my mother I never knew about. Beneath the strong, successful image, there is an uncertain woman. Mom and I are alike. She secretly feels like a nothing, the way I do. It seems impossible because she's so talented. Could it be that I'm talented and creative, too? Mrs. Canby is right. I have to find out what's special about me.

Narrator 1: The next day, Jean is in the living room when Lisl comes home from school. Louis goes into the kitchen to fix dinner.

Jean: He hardly ever talks to me. I guess he doesn't love me anymore.

Lisl: Of course he loves you, Mom. It's just . . . I'll talk to you.

Jean: What's that paper sticking out of your book?

Lisl: It's an essay about freedom. We all had to write one for a contest.

Jean: May I read it?

(Lisl is a little embarrassed, but she gives the essay to her mother. Her mother reads it and looks at her seriously.)

Jean: Lisl, this is very good. I didn't know you could write this well. *(She smiles at Lisl.)* I wrote a poem once. I was ten years

old. It was just after my parents died, and I felt like the loneliest person in the world.

Narrator 1: A few days later, Lisl goes to see Mrs. Canby again.

Lisl: I never knew my mother could feel lonely or insecure.

Mrs. Canby: You've learned a lot about your mom. But you haven't told me anything about yourself.

Lisl: Well, I do have some news. My essay was picked to represent our school in a contest.

Mrs. Canby: Congratulations!

Lisl: I guess I've always liked to express myself in writing. Sometimes, when I feel a lot of pressure, I put my feelings on paper. It helps me to see things more clearly.

Mrs. Canby: Things about yourself?

Lisl: Yes, and about other things, too. *(She pauses.)* I see Mom slipping away, and I know it's only a matter of time. But all life ends sometime. I guess you should enjoy it while you can. And you don't have to do a million things to be happy—just a few things that you really like.

Mrs. Canby: Graduation is coming, and then you're going to be more on your own. Do you still feel like a nothing?

Lisl: No. I guess I'm me. Maybe in my own way I am special. I'm no superstar or anything, but I'm me.

Mrs. Canby: That's all any of us can be.

Narrator 2: Several weeks later, Lisl is in Jean's bedroom. She is showing her mother her cap and gown she'll wear for graduation.

Lisl (*looking in a mirror*): I think it fits just right, don't you? Of course it has to be pressed.

(*She suddenly realizes her mother isn't listening. She turns and sees Jean staring into space. Lisl goes over and takes her hand.*)

Lisl: Mama? What can we do? Please tell us.

Jean (*turning away from her*): Let me die.

Narrator 1: The next day, Lisl is taking a typing test. While the teacher dictates a letter, the students type it. Lisl is not listening. She is thinking about her mother and typing her thoughts. We hear her saying what she's typing.

Lisl's Voice: What do you do when you know it's coming to an end? How could you think of all the good things in life and know you could never see them again? That's why she turned away from me. It's easier to stare at the wall than to look at things she loves.

Narrator 2: The teacher has stopped dictating and the students have stopped typing. Lisl, not paying attention, keeps typing. The teacher accuses her of cheating.

Lisl: I wasn't cheating! You know I'm not a cheater! It's just . . . it's my mother! She's dying! She's actually dying! (*She runs from the room, crying.*)

Narrator 1: Jean is taken to the hospital a week before graduation. In the hospital room, Jane and Lisl sit near the bed. Jim and Louis are staring out the window. Jean opens her eyes and tries to say something.

Lisl: Mom? What is it, Mom?
(*Louis and Jim come over.*)

Louis: Jean, don't try to talk. You need to rest.

Lisl: No, Dad. She wants to say something. What is it, Mom?
(*She leans over the bed, close to Jean. Jean tries to speak, but only makes some sounds.*)

Lisl: I think I understand, Mom. You know we love you. Now you want us to know that you love us.

(*Jean relaxes. She nods and holds out her hands. Lisl takes one hand, and Louis takes the other. Jean drifts off to sleep.*)

Narrator 2: Later, Lisl meets Mrs. Canby in the hospital coffee shop.

Mrs. Canby: It's any minute now, isn't it? (*Lisl nods.*) How are you holding up?

Lisl: Okay, but I'm confused. Part of me wishes she were dead, so the suffering would end. Part of me wishes she would never die.

Mrs. Canby: Remember, you'll be able to choose the things you liked best about her and keep them. You'll pass them on to your own children. (*There is a long pause.*) How did you do in the essay contest?

Lisl: I lost. But my essay was good, and it taught me who I am. I'm Lisl Gilbert, the writer.

Narrator 1: Lisl goes back to her mother's hospital room. Her family is standing outside with two nurses. Jim tries to stop Lisl from entering the room.

Jim: Lisl —

Lisl: I know. I want to see her.

(He steps aside, and she goes in. Jean's eyes are closed, and she shows no signs of life.)

Lisl: I hope you can hear me, Mom. I just want you to know I love you. *(She begins to cry softly.)* I've learned a lot about myself lately, and I've learned a lot about you. I wish you could have stayed around longer, so we could have known each other as adults. Maybe in some ways, we'll always be together. I hope so.

Narrator 2: On graduation day, Lisl comes down to the living room in her cap and gown.

Jane: You look beautiful.

Louis: You look so much like your mother. *(He holds out a gift for her.)* This is for you, sweetheart. The wrapping isn't very neat. It's the best she could do in her condition.

Lisl *(taking the gift)*: Is it from Mom?

Louis: Yes. She wanted to give you something.

(Lisl unwraps the package. Inside, she finds several beautiful books with blank pages to be filled with writing. She reads the note on the top.)

Lisl: "In case I'm not here when you graduate, this is for you, dear Lisl. You're going to be a fine writer some day and make us all very proud. It's just a matter of time." ◆

READING CHECK

Answer the following questions about "Just A Matter of Time." You may want to check your answers by reviewing details from the play.

1. Why did Jean have to check into the hospital?

2. How did Lisl learn that her mother had only a short time to live? How did Lisl take the news?

3. What advice did Jane give Lisl to help her cope with her mother's illness?

4. Who was Mrs. Canby? Why did she come to visit Lisl's family?

5. Why did Lisl's essay on freedom turn out to be important to her?

6. Why did Lisl's teacher accuse her of cheating in typing class? What was Lisl really doing?

7. What did Lisl's mother give her as a graduation gift? Why was this gift so special to Lisl?

WHAT DO YOU THINK?

1. Why do you think that Lisl avoided telling even her best friend about her mother's illness? If you were Lisl's friend what do you think that you would have done to help her?

2. In what ways do you think that Lisl and her mother were alike? In what ways were they very different from each other?

3. Lisl tells Mrs. Canby that "you don't have to do a million things to be happy — just a few things that you really like." Explain why Lisl's saying this helped her better accept herself and her mother's dying.

VOCABULARY CHECK

Read the following sentences and choose the correct meaning of each word in **bold print.** Then write each word and its meaning on your paper.

1. Jean was part of the art **faculty.**
   (teaching staff, painting party)

2. Sometimes even people who are talented feel **insecure.**
   (not famous, not safe)

3. Lisl walked alone down the school **corridor.**
   (cafeteria, hallway)

4. The **cemetery** was a peaceful place.
   (formal garden, graveyard)

STRATEGY CHECK

The paragraph below is based on the play, "Just A Matter of Time." Choose a word that makes sense to fill in each blank. Use the the rest of the paragraph and your knowledge of the play to help you. Then write the whole paragraph on your paper.

Lisl always thought that her mother was one of the most t____ people she knew. But when her mother becomes very ill with c____, she soon stops painting. At first Lisl won't accept the fact that her mother is going to d____. With the help of a social w____, named Mrs. Canby, Lisl is finally able to face the truth. In the end, Lisl knows that she will be able to go on living without her m____.

"POEMS ABOUT IT'S ABOUT TIME"

The two poems that you will read here reveal the ideas of people who feel that time is passing too quickly. In her poem, "Marie Lucille," Gwendolyn Brooks describes the way one girl feels about growing up. In "There Isn't Time!" Eleanor Farjeon describes a feeling that most people have experienced at one time or another.

WORDS TO KNOW

The words in **bold print,** are from "Poems About It's About Time." Study each word and its meaning carefully.

When Marie Lucille was young she liked to eat **licorice.**
   licorice — a chewy candy that gets its flavor from the root of a certain plant

The poet was proud of the new **rhyme** she had written.
   rhyme — poem that includes a regular repetition of sounds

MARIE LUCILLE

by GWENDOLYN BROOKS

That clock is ticking
Me away!
The me that only
Yesterday
Ate peanuts, jam and
Licorice
Is gone already.
And this is
'Cause nothing's putting
Back, each day,
The me that clock is
Ticking away.

THERE ISN'T TIME!

by ELEANOR FARJEON

There isn't time, there isn't time
To do the things I want to do,
With all the mountain-tops to climb,
And all the woods to wander through,
And all the seas to sail upon,
And everywhere there is to go,
And all the people, every one
Who lives upon the earth, to know.
There's only time, there's only time
To know a few, and do a few,
And then sit down and make a rhyme
About the rest I want to do.

WHAT DO YOU THINK?

1. What does Marie Lucille mean when she says "the clock is ticking me away?" In what ways are you different from the way you were five years ago? What do you think will be different about the way you look, act, and feel five years from now?

2. In "There Isn't Time!", what are some of the things that the speaker in the poem wishes that she had time to do? What are some of the things you would do if you had more time?

3. Why do you think that the speaker in the poem decided to write about the things she will probably not have time to do? When you feel that you have too much to do, how do you decide which things are the most important?

VOCABULARY CHECK

Read the following sentences and choose the correct meaning for each word in **bold print.** Then write each word and its meaning on your paper.

1. The book contained a **rhyme** she had never read before.
    (rhythm, poem)

2. Marie Lucille no longer likes **licorice.**
    (a kind of candy, a kind of liquid)

READING REVIEW

"It's About Time" shows that time affects your life in many ways. Choose the best ending for each sentence below. Then write the complete sentence on your paper.

1. In the story "Lucky Break," Toby gets a lucky break when he ____.
   a. takes karate lessons
   b. forgets to set his alarm clock
   c. becomes friends with Hulk
   d. gets sent to the principal's office

2. In the article "Nature's Amazing Clocks," the author points out that all animals ____.
   a. can tell time by the sun
   b. have their own rhythms
   c. sleep during the day
   d. have been used in experiments

3. In the story "My Kind of Watch," Clarence Day explains that his father would not give him his own watch until he learned how to ____.
   a. be on time
   b. replace watch crystals
   c. play the piano
   d. take care of heirlooms

4. In the story "My Kind of Watch," Clarence is finally able to return the delicate, old watch his mother gave him when he ____.
   a. accidentally breaks the watch
   b. saves money to buy a watch
   c. explains his feelings to her
   d. gets a watch from his father

5. In the play "Just a Matter of Time," Lisl has a hard time facing the fact that her mother ____.
   a. is not a talented painter
   b. is dying of cancer
   c. does not want to see her graduate
   d. is going to teach art

6. By the end of the play, Lisl knows that her mother was proud of her and believed Lisl would ____.
   a. become a fine writer
   b. never develop cancer
   c. develop talent as a painter
   d. graduate from college

VOCABULARY REVIEW

Review some words from *It's About Time* that show how people move or change over time. Choose a word from the list to replace the words in **bold print** in each sentence below. Then write the new sentences on your paper.

observing	**spurred**	**cope**
dawdling	**sprinted**	**reform**

1. Toby had been **watching** Hulk for a long time, and he was worried.

2. Clarence had to **deal with** the problem of always being late.

3. Lisl **ran** home to tell her mother the news about her winning the essay contest.

4. Toby kept **moving slowly** because he wanted to get to school just as the bell rang.

5. Although the principal punished him, Toby did not promise to **change his bad behavior.**

6. The sadness Lisl had to face in life somehow **encouraged** her desire to become a writer.

WRITING ABOUT
ITS ABOUT TIME

1. Use the card catalog at your library to find out more about the habits of bees, bats or fiddler crabs and how their inner clocks tell them what to do.

2. Imagine that you are Clarence Day. Write a letter to your mother explaining why you do not want to use the watch she gave you. In your letter try to persuade your mother to take back her gift. You may want to make a list of your reasons before you begin the letter.

3. Lisl was able to deal with some bad things that happened to her because she had many pleasant memories of things that she and her family did together. Writing about your memories is one way to preserve them over time. Pick a pleasant memory you have of something that happened recently or long ago. Write a paragraph about this time so you can remember it always.

UNIT

·5·

WINNING AND LOSING

Everyone likes to be a winner. That's only natural. Everyone likes to win a prize, a contest, an athletic event, an argument. But, sometimes, losing can also have its positive side. In this unit, you will read about some winners, some losers, and some people who discover that it is possible to be both a winner and a loser at the same time.

In the story "The Grand Prize," Mitchell wins something he had always dreamed about. But not even Mitchell's dreams can prepare him for the surprising events that follow. In "A Private Place," Beth is about to lose something she values more than anything else. It takes another person to help Beth see that winning and losing are not that far apart.

"Aunt Susan's Trial" is the true story of a famous woman who seems to lose a battle when she is found guilty of a crime. But what she actually wins changes history. The last selection, "Amigo Brothers," tells the story of two close friends who face a contest that only one of them can win. And the price of winning may be the end of a friendship.

Each selection in the unit is about a different kind of winning and losing. Yet, all the selections are alike in one way. They show that when you know that you have done your best or what you know is right, you always come out a real winner.

UNDERSTANDING WORDS IN SENTENCES

Words About Winning and Losing. Certain words describe what happens when people win or lose. Six words that have to do with winning and losing are in **bold print** in the sentences below. All the words are used in this unit. Use the sentence pairs to help you choose the correct meaning of each word in **bold print.** Then write the word and its meaning on your paper.

1. The winner and his family were driven to the city in a **limousine.** They rode along in comfort in the back seat.
    (a decorated plane, a large, closed automobile)

2. The check was presented to the winner in a special **ceremony.** Everyone had to stand in a certain place.
    (a musical play, a formal event)

3. For a while, Beth felt that her family had **deserted** her. She was alone with her troubles.
    (punished, left)

4. Susan believed that the **penalty** was unfair. Why should she be punished for doing the right thing?
    (mistake or crime, fine or punishment)

5. The boys fought in many practice bouts before the **tournament.** Each dreamed of being the champion.
    (series of contests, group of athletes)

6. The champion had to face a new **challenger** in the ring. Only one of them could win the title.
    (one who tests another, one who wins a contest)

◆ INTRODUCING ◆

"THE GRAND PRIZE"

Mitchell's hobby is entering contests by mail. He buys a lot of stamps and never wins. But then, one day, he gets a phone call, and everything changes. Find out what unusual prize Mitchell wins, and how his whole family — and his parrot — discover what it means to win the grand prize.

WORDS TO KNOW

The words in **bold print** are from "The Grand Prize." Study each word and its meaning carefully.

Mitchell learned that the winning entry would be drawn from a **replica** of a box of Dazzle Detergent.
    replica — an exact copy, a duplicate

Winners of the Dazzle Rama sweepstakes were going to be **notified** by letter.
    notified — told, informed

Mitchell's mother didn't trust the caller and wanted to make sure the contest was **legitimate.**
    legitimate — lawful, according to the rules

Pictures would be taken, and the caller hoped that the contest winner was **photogenic.**
    photogenic — looking good in photographs

The view from the top floor of the skyscraper was **spectacular.**
    spectacular — amazing to see

THE GRAND PRIZE

by MARJORIE WEINMAN SHARMAT

Not too long ago, I had a normal life. Two parents, an older sister to fight with, a best friend, a girl in school I'd like to know better, a parrot named Dennis, and a hobby.

Maybe I should have mentioned my hobby first: I enter sweepstakes contests by mail. My sister Lynda said I reminded her of a scientist about to go mad. My mother said I should have a hobby where I could get some fresh air. My father kept a running total of the price of my stamps on his pocket calculator. Nobody liked my hobby.

They didn't understand. I love to enter sweepstakes. I love the look of the entry blanks. I love to read "You May Already Have Won . . ." I love the small print that explains all the rules. I love the pictures of the prizes. I love it when our family name is printed in, as if we'd already won, even though Mom says a computer does that.

I must have entered 60 or 70 sweepstakes when I got the Dazzle-Rama Sweepstakes in the mail. It was addressed to me. I must be on a sweepstakes mailing list. I wondered if they'd cross me out if they knew I was only 12 years old. This contest was sponsored by Dazzle Detergent, the detergent that cleans and irons your clothes. But I didn't have to buy any detergent to enter. All I had to do was fill out an entry blank. This was a snap. A lot of the sweepstakes have numbers to match up or things to scratch off. The winning entry would be drawn from a five-foot replica of a box of Dazzle Detergent. The Grand Prize was $250,000. There were 150 prizes in all. I entered.

The day I dropped my Dazzle-Rama

Sweepstakes entry in the mailbox was just another school day. Lynda saw the envelope in my hand as I was leaving for school and said, "Is this the day you make us filthy rich? Ha, ha."

My mother said, "Try to get the minimum daily requirement of fresh air today."

My father totaled up my stamp expenses for the week. He said I'd make us poor trying to get rich.

I walk to school every day with my best friend Roseanne Rich, who lives across the street. She always watches while I mail my sweepstakes entries. And she always laughs and shakes her head. "Another one?" she

said that day. "Don't you ever give up? You've never won anything."

"Not yet."

"It won't happen, Mitch. Do you know how many thousands of people enter those contests?"

I couldn't tell Roseanne that the odds of winning the $250,000 Grand Prize in the Dazzle-Rama Sweepstakes were one in 19,265,000. I saw it in the information sheet.

At school, things weren't any better. I sit beside Melissa Gertz in some of my classes. Melissa never kidded me about the sweepstakes because Melissa never spoke to me. She's one of those stuck-up girls who only talk to certain kids. I wasn't one of them. I wished I was. We'd been sitting side by side for two months. Sometimes she'd turn her head and look at me as if I were dead and she was just waiting for my body to be removed. Couldn't she smile?

Once she almost smiled. It was when we were all giving talks on hobbies. Naturally, I gave a talk on entering sweepstakes and how I was going to get rich. Mr. Devon, our teacher, likes me because I print neatly, so he said. "Very good, Mitchell." But the kids roared. Roseanne collects lizards, which I think is weird, but nobody laughed at her.

I tried to keep quiet about my hobby after that, but it was hard. The sweepstakes were always in my mind. I had this same dream over and over.

"Is this Mitchell Dartmouth?"

"Yes."

"Do you live at 112 Fuller Street?"

"Yes."

"And did you enter the Dazzle-Rama Sweepstakes sponsored by Dazzle Detergent, the detergent that cleans and irons your clothes?"

"Yes."

"Congratulations. You have just won the $250,000 Grand Prize."

Then one day it really happened. I answered the phone and heard a voice ask, "Is this Mitchell Dartmouth?"

"Yes."

"Do you live at 112 Fuller Street?"

"Yes."

"And did you enter the Dazzle-Rama Sweepstakes sponsored by Dazzle Detergent, the detergent that cleans and irons your clothes?"

"Yes."

"Congratulations. You have just won the $250,000 Grand Prize."

This was not a dream. It was four months after I had entered the Dazzle-Rama Sweepstakes. When the telephone rang, I answered it. And that was the conversation. Actually, those might not have been the exact words. But it was close. It was also, I figured, a joke. "You can't fool me," I said. "Winners are supposed to be notified by mail." One of the kids from school must have been having some fun.

"This isn't a joke," the voice said. "You will be notified officially by mail."

"Just a minute," I said. I ran to get my mother. If the call was from a kid, he'd hang up when he heard my mom's voice.

"Take this, Mom."

My mother picked up the receiver. She looked puzzled. She said, "Hello. This is Mrs. Dartmouth." Then she listened.

She turned to me and asked, "Did you enter some contest about cleaning and ironing clothes?"

"Sure. I entered the Dazzle-Rama Sweepstakes."

She spoke into the telephone. "If this isn't legitimate, I'm contacting the Better Business Bureau, the attorney general's office, and the Office of Consumer Affairs."

I whispered to my mother, "A real contest runs a clearance check on big winners to see if they've won before or to see if they're crooks and all that stuff."

My mother spoke into the phone again. "Mitchell says this is a phony call because you didn't run a clearance check on him."

Pause. "You *did*? We didn't notice. Oh, we're not *supposed* to notice. Isn't that rather sneaky?"

Another pause. "I see. Yes. I see. I understand. Really? *Really*? It's true? *True*?" My mother turned to me and screamed, "You won $250,000!"

I knew this wasn't a dream because my mother never screams in my dreams.

Back to the telephone. My mother was saying, "What? Oh, 12 last October. I see. Well, no real problem. It's really his money, isn't it?"

What was she talking about? A catch, I knew it.

"Hold on," she said to the receiver. She turned to me. "The rules say that any prize won by a minor will be awarded in the name of a parent or legal guardian. But, of course, Dad and I aren't going to keep *your* money."

Mom was back on the phone. "The publicity? Oh, yes, he's very photogenic."

Back to me. "They want the winner's publicity to center on you. Okay?"

"Huh?"

Mom turned back to the phone. "He says that's wonderful."

I just stood there in shock. I couldn't believe that I won! I wondered what $250,000 looked like. If they paid you in

pennies, would they fill the whole room? Or the house? Or the neighborhood? What would $250,000 in nickels look like? Or dimes? What if they paid in stamps? I could plaster them all over the house. My father would go crazy trying to peel them off.

My mother would never send me out into the fresh air again.

Lynda would stop making fun of me. She'd start begging me for money.

Roseanne would stop laughing at my hobby.

Two men from Dazzle Detergent arrived Friday afternoon, right after I got home from school. Mom had fixed up our place to make them feel at home. She went out and bought boxes and boxes of Dazzle Detergent and stood them up all over the house.

The men from Dazzle pulled up in a limousine driven by a chauffeur in a uniform. Mom, Dad, Lynda, and I were looking out the window, watching it drive up to our house.

"We shouldn't be doing this," said Lynda. "We have to start acting classy. We've got about one minute to get rid of these gross detergent boxes. Rich people don't have detergent boxes in their living rooms."

"They stay," said Mom. "When you're older, you'll recognize atmosphere when you see it."

"They make me sneeze," said Lynda.

Mom let the two Dazzle guys into the house. There were five boxes of Dazzle just inside the front door. The men didn't seem to notice. The man in front grabbed my

hand, shook it up and down, and kicked over a box of detergent. He didn't look down. He introduced himself as "the man on the telephone, Roger Hemingway. Everyone calls me Rog. I'm Vice-president of Marketing for Dazzle Detergent."

Rog was ticking off items about himself like someone describing a product. Then he introduced the man in back of him as "Al."

Rog and Al looked at all the boxes of detergent. "What a dazzling idea," said Rog.

I heard Lynda groan.

Mom gestured for Rog and Al to sit down. They each took a chair, since the sofa was occupied. They checked for spilled detergent before sitting.

Rog spoke to me. "Young man, we have big plans for you. This afternoon, you'll be given your check at our corporate headquarters. The media will be there. Tomorrow, a television crew will follow you around while you get new clothes. You're a very lucky young man."

Rog kept right on talking. "But before we get going, I'd like to get a bit of background information on you and your family."

He and Al took turns asking us about 100 questions. Rog's last question was, "How does it feel to win $250,000, Mitchell?"

"Feels real good," I said.

I think he wanted a better answer than that.

"What do you plan to do with the

money?" asked Al.

I wanted to give Al a great answer. Maybe I could earn him a title or a last name.

But Mom spoke up. "That's to be determined," she said, "by wiser heads than ours."

Rog noticed my parrot in his cage over in a corner.

"Does your parrot talk?"

"His name is Dennis," I said. "He's never said a word. But he's a wonderful pet."

"He *looks* wonderful," said Rog. "You must be very proud of him."

I began to doubt that Rog was a sincere person.

"Why not bring the parrot along?" said Al. "It's a good angle."

"I agree," said Dad. "Excellent strategy."

Rog was staring at Dennis. "A family pet. Very heartwarming. And a nice change from dogs." Rog stood up. "Well, shall we leave?"

We all started to walk toward the door.

"Don't forget the bird," said Rog.

Dad carried Dennis in his cage. He was whispering to him, "*Dazzle. Dazzle. Dazzle.* Remember what I taught you. You can say it. You're smart, Dennis."

We walked out to the limousine. The chauffeur opened the door for us. Mom peered inside. "This is spectacular!"

"Nothing is too good for the $250,000 kid," said Rog.

I wore a new shirt washed in Dazzle for the ceremony. That was another of my mother's ideas. She wanted to be able to say truthfully, "Mitchell's shirt was washed in Dazzle." The shirt was so new, it had never been worn. It looked clean *before* it went into the wash. And it sure looked more ironed than when it came out. Dazzle claims to iron your clothes, but it doesn't say what they look like afterwards.

The Dazzle corporate offices were in a skyscraper downtown. After our elevator ride, we got ushered from room to room and up and down stairs. All along the way, we were introduced to people. Everyone acted as if they knew me very well. But they paid more attention to Dennis. At last we were in this big room with television cameras. There were lots of people standing around. There was a uniformed man and about a dozen well-dressed men and women, plus the television crew.

I was told to stand next to this tremendous box of Dazzle. I bet there wasn't any Dazzle in it. The box and I were about the same height. My parents and Lynda stood just behind me.

"Hold up the bird cage, Mr. Dartmouth," Rog said. "Higher, please."

Dad looked proud. He hoisted the cage above his head.

"A bit lower, Mr. Dartmouth," said Rog.

While Dad was raising and lowering the cage, Lynda was trying to peek into the Dazzle box. I was standing under a spotlight. There were other lights all over the place. It was hot.

Rog motioned to the television people. The camera started to zoom in on me.

Suddenly a man appeared from behind a curtain and stuck something in my hand. His voice boomed out, "Congratulations!" He kept shaking my hand while the cameras moved in closer. Unfortunately, he was shaking the hand that was holding the check. I could feel the check squashing.

Rog was signaling me with his arms. He wanted me to hold up the check for the camera. I held it up. Rog made a face. Dazzle, the detergent that washes and irons your clothes, sure awarded one wrecked check.

Rog waved for the cameras to stop. "Could we do that again, please, with a fresh check?"

"You mean I get another $250,000?" I asked.

Rog tried to smile. "The computer would have a heart attack."

Rog and the check man put their heads together. "We'll be right back," Rog announced. They returned a few minutes later. The check man was holding a piece of paper. It looked like a check from where I was standing.

Rog turned to the television people, "We're doing the ceremony again. But don't go beyond this spot." Rog drew an imaginary line on the floor.

The check man went behind the curtain and walked out again. He stuck the paper in my hand. This time he didn't shake my hand.

Rog signaled for me to hold up the paper. He signaled the television crew not to come any closer.

I looked up at the paper I was holding. It was smooth and crisp. It said, FIVE DOLLAR DISCOUNT COUPON FOR MOE'S UPTOWN GARAGE.

Rog signaled to Mom and Dad and Lynda. I got hugs and kisses for the camera. Dad gave me a half hug because he was holding up Dennis's cage in one hand.

Suddenly Dennis squawked, "Dazzle!"

"Beautiful!!!" said Rog. "This, ladies and gentlemen, is Dennis, the family pet."

All the cameras zoomed in on Dennis while I just stood there holding my discount coupon.

"Say something else, Dennis." A reporter

stood by the cage with a tape recorder.

"Speech, speech," said another reporter.

You'd think Dennis had won the Dazzle-Rama Sweepstakes.

Dennis clammed up. So the reporters turned to me and asked what I planned to do with the money. I answered before my parents could say a word. "Well, I'll probably give $200,000 of it to my favorite charities. The $50,000 that's left, I keep for myself."

When the ceremony was over, Rog said, "I hope you won't get pestered by a bunch of characters wanting some of your money."

"I don't have any money," I said. "I have a discount coupon from Moe's Uptown Garage. Where is my check?"

"*What*? Where did it go?"

"That's what I am asking you. I think you dropped it on the floor."

The television cameras started to roll while Mom, Dad, Lynda, me, the check man, Rog, and most of the well-dressed men and women of Dazzle got down on their hands and knees to look for the check.

Somebody found it in the replica of the Dazzle Detergent box. We were trying to figure out how it got there when Dennis squawked, "Dazzle!" again.

The cameras zoomed in on him.

Dennis had turned into a big show-off.

The television crew filmed us as we got back into the limousine and were driven off. Rog followed us in their van.

"I can hardly wait for them to film you trying on your clothes, Mitchell," said Mom.

"Wait a minute. Do they go into dressing rooms? Do they see you in your underwear?"

"That won't get on television," said Dad. "They only use a small part of what they film, and I'm sure they won't use *that*."

"This is getting good," said Lynda.

The chauffeur, who had not spoken a word to us, suddenly turned around and said, "No underwear shots."

"Whew!"

The store was crowded. "You go first," Rog said. My family and Rog and Al and the television crew followed me like a parade. Everyone stared at us. At *me*. I liked this much better. I loved it! The cameras were focused on me alone. We marched toward the boys' department. Rog and Al led the way.

A boy came up to me. "May I have your autograph?" he asked. He was holding a piece of paper. Another boy was with him. "Who's he?" the second boy asked.

"I don't know," the first boy answered.

Rog put his arm on my shoulder. "This is Mitchell Dartmouth. He just won $250,000 in the Dazzle-Rama Sweepstakes."

"Is Dazzle-Rama a video game?" asked the second boy.

"No," I said.

The boys shrugged and walked away.

Mom rushed up to me. "Your first autograph!" she said. "Isn't that exciting?"

"They didn't want it," I said.

"They *almost* wanted it, son," said Dad.

I was glad to get to the dressing room where I could pull the curtain. ◆

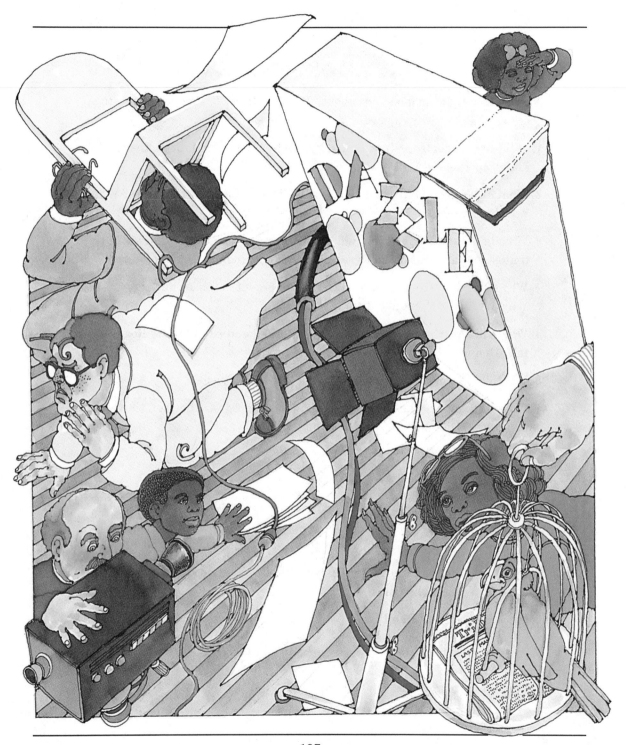

READING CHECK

Answer the following questions about "The Grand Prize." You may want to check your answers by reviewing details in the story.

1. What did Mitchell's sister think of his hobby? Why didn't his mother and father appove of it?

2. What did Mitchell have to do to enter the Dazzle Rama sweepstakes? What was the Grand Prize?

3. Why did Mitchell put his mother on the phone when he got a call about the contest? What was Mitchell's reaction when he knew he had really won?

4. Why did Mrs. Darmouth spread Dazzle Detergent boxes around the house? Why did Lynda think about this?

5. Where did Mitchell and his family go with Rog and Al? Why did Rog want to take Dennis?

6. What did Dennis do that amused the people from Dazzle?

7. What happened to the check from Dazzle? What did Mitchell tell the reporters he planned to do with his money?

WHAT DO YOU THINK?

1. What would be the most important thing you would do with $250,000?

2. Do you think that entering sweepstakes contests is a good way to make money? Why, or why not?

3. If you had a parrot like Dennis, what would you teach him to say?

VOCABULARY CHECK

Read the following sentences and choose the correct meaning of each work in **bold print.** Then write each word and its meaning on your paper.

1. Mitchell dreamed that a caller **notified** him about winning the Grand Prize.
   (informed, interested)

2. Mrs. Darmouth thought that putting Dazzle Detergent boxes around the house was a **spectacular** idea.
   (responsible, amazing)

3. Lynda tried to see what was in the huge **replica** of the Dazzle box.
   (copy, drawing)

4. When Mrs. Darmouth realized that the contest was **legitimate,** she turned to Mitchell and screamed.
   (lawful, wonderful)

5. The people running a contest prefer the winners to be **photogenic.**
   (able to win, photograph well)

STRATEGY CHECK

The paragraph below is based on the story "The Grand Prize." Choose a word that makes sense to fill in each blank. Use the rest of the paragraph and your knowledge of the story to help you. Then write the whole paragraph on your paper.

   Mitchell Darmouth was very surprised to hear that he had ____ the Grand Prize in a contest. His whole ____ took part in a ceremony for television. Mr. Darmouth brought Dennis in his ____. The reporters asked Mitchell many ____. They tried to get Dennis to ____ While all this was happening, the ____ from Dazzle disappeared.

"A PRIVATE PLACE"

Beth knows that her grandfather is old and can't take care of himself anymore. But there must be many ways to solve that problem, Beth figures. Why must her parents pick this way — inviting her grandfather into their home and her room? Now all kinds of things are bound to happen, and Beth is not prepared for any of them.

WORDS TO KNOW

The words in **bold print** are from "A Private Place." Study each word and its meaning carefully.

Beth was **impatient** when waiting for something to happen.
    impatient — feeling annoyed because of a delay

A plastic **flamingo** sat on the lawn in front of the house.
    flamingo — a large bird with long legs

Beth **blurted** out the words she had held inside for weeks.
    blurted — spoke suddenly without thinking

Beth's father shot a **glare** her way when she tried to leave the room.
    glare — fierce, angry look

She decided to **barge** into the room, without even knocking.
    barge — enter without warning

Granddad probably did not want to be thought of as an **intruder** in the room.
    intruder — someone who enters without an invitation

When she looked into her grandfather's eyes, Beth saw the family **resemblance.**
    resemblance — likeness

A PRIVATE PLACE

by PHYLLIS FAIR COWELL

There are two kinds of waiting, and I don't like either kind. Waiting for something I want makes me anxious and impatient. Waiting for something I don't want makes me nervous and angry.

I especially don't like waiting for something I don't want . . . but waiting was all I could do. It was going to happen, whether I liked it or not. So I pressed my nose against the window and watched the rain.

Across the street, small lawns grew green in front of small houses. A plastic flamingo balanced in the grass, and a toddler splashed through puddles in the walk. They both seemed happy with this dreary day. Not me.

On the corner, an apartment building echoed my mood. Two windows, lit against the dark afternoon, stared back like eyes. Rain streaked down the building's face like tears. That was more like me.

Behind me, my mother folded laundry.

She had been working all day, and I should have helped. Instead, I asked the question one more time.

"Why does he have to come live with us?" I mumbled at the window pane.

My mother sighed, then spoke in a tightened voice. "You're not a four-year-old, you know. You don't have to ask the same thing over and over." She sighed once more. "Your grandfather just can't take care of himself anymore."

I turned around and blurted out the words I'd held inside for weeks. "There are homes for people like that!"

She dropped a towel and stared at me. Her voice grew lower as she spoke. "Don't say that again," she said.

I turned back to the window, the rain, and my thoughts. It wasn't that I hated my grandfather. I didn't remember him enough to hate him. Years ago, when I was little, I'd spent summers on his farm. But he was always busy — working from dawn until past dark. Most of the time I was free to explore and to be as wild as I pleased. Sometimes I helped my grandmother in the house.

But that was long ago, and those memories were dim. All I really remembered was the smell of the pigs and the look of the pictures. There were so many pictures, they seemed to cover every wall. They were old-fashioned pictures with lots of trees . . . as if there weren't enough trees around the house already.

When my grandmother died, I stopped going there. Only my dad went, once a year, to visit his father. Last year, he came back with worry on his face.

"He can't do it anymore," Dad said as he sank into a chair.

"Who?" I asked.

"Your granddad, Beth. He can't keep working like that. He's tired all the time and he looks sick."

"We have to do something," I said. "We have to help."

That's what I said . . . then.

No, I didn't hate my grandfather. And I really didn't care if he lived in this house. He could live anywhere he wanted — except in my room. And that's just the place he was going.

That room meant a lot to me. It was my own private place.

We live in a city house — small and close to its neighbors. There are no rooms to spare and no space to add on. Privacy is hard to come by. So I was lucky when I convinced Mom to give up her old sewing room. It was tiny . . . but it was mine.

I got a job after school, and most of my money went into that room. I bought the red curtains and rug and furry pillows. I painted it bright yellow and put wild posters on the walls. It was me, from top to bottom.

Now I was being tucked into a pink and white corner of my little sister's room. It just wasn't fair. I had a right to be angry.

Anger did not keep it from happening, though. I saw our car turn the corner and pull up to the curb. My father jumped out and rushed to the other side. I watched as he tried to juggle an umbrella and help the old man out of the car.

Granddad seemed smaller than I remembered. His steps were uncertain, and he moved toward the house very slowly. It just wasn't slow enough for me.

"Come on." My mother was insistent as she jerked me away from the window.

At the door, there were hugs and kisses. I pretended to be glad to see him. But everyone else was saying, "Welcome." I just couldn't say that word because I didn't mean it.

My little sister, Jill, suddenly appeared with a handful of flowers and a grin on her face. She told Granddad how she had been helping all day to get ready for him. I could have strangled her.

We all moved into the kitchen where Granddad drank hot tea. They all sat down — all except me. I tried to back out of the

room, but my father shot a glare my way. I stayed, but nothing could make me sit down.

They talked awhile about nothing important. Every now and then, Granddad stared out the window. Maybe his mind was drifting. Maybe he was shocked to see the city streets after years in the country.

Then he said he was tired and wanted to lie down. My mother helped him up and showed him down the hall to his room. My room!

Only anger held off my tears.

I wandered into the living room in a daze. I was standing there when my mother came storming in with my stereo.

"I told you to get your things out of that room!" she snapped. "This is in his way."

She said no more, but left me to take care of the stereo. I did. I plugged it in and put on a record. My mother came right back to the living room and turned it off.

"What are you doing?" she demanded. "He's trying to take a nap."

I exploded. "Don't I belong anywhere in this house?" I yelled. I didn't wait for an answer. I ran to my sister's room and locked the door.

As soon as I did, the tears came. I buried my face in a pillow and sobbed. Between sobs, I thought of how my family had deserted me. No one cared what I was going through. All they cared about was that old man. He had it made now — food service, laundry service, maid service. He must think this is heaven.

A banging on the door disturbed me. "Hey, open up! You can't lock me out of my own room!" Jill cried.

"Oh, no?" I yelled through the door. "What makes you any different from me? Get lost!"

"At least let me have my radio," she pleaded.

I unlocked the door and she pushed her way in to grab some weird looking object. It had a face and ears. And she called that a radio! On the way out, she stuck out her tongue before I could slam the door shut.

Suddenly, I thought of my own radio. I had a right to have it, but it was one of the things I had left in my old room. If Jill could barge in here, then I could barge in there.

I knew he was sleeping and I might wake him. I didn't care. If he woke up, I would tell him how I felt. I would tell him what he'd done to me. Maybe he didn't know and never intended to be an intruder. If he knew, maybe he'd leave. I had to have it out with him sooner or later. Sooner was good enough for me.

The door was not locked but I opened it slowly. What I saw was so ridiculous, I almost laughed. He looked so out of place in my brightly colored room. He lay face down, under an old gray blanket he must have brought with him. It made him look older and grayer somehow. Above his head hung my motorcycle poster. The cycle looked as if it were about to roar right over him.

"Trees," he mumbled. His voice startled me, but I thought he must be talking in his sleep. Then he added, "Can't see any here."

I stood there in silence, trying to figure out if this was really sleep talk. His body did not appear to move at all. If he had not spoken I would not have been sure he was alive.

"It hurts, doesn't it?" he said. He wasn't talking in his sleep.

"What?" I said.

"Giving up your own place."

Now I didn't know what to say. I sure couldn't argue with that. They were the only words I had heard all day that made sense.

"They say you get used to it," he said. "I don't know. I had my own place for more than 40 years."

"How did you know this was my room?" I asked.

He laughed and turned over to face me. I looked back at eyes like mine. It wasn't just family resemblance. They were eyes that had cried.

"This room looks like you," he said. "Oh, I remember how you were — bright and bold." He chuckled, then his face became sad. "My place looked like me."

I was getting upset. Our talk wasn't supposed to be like this. I was supposed to attack. I was supposed to fight for my

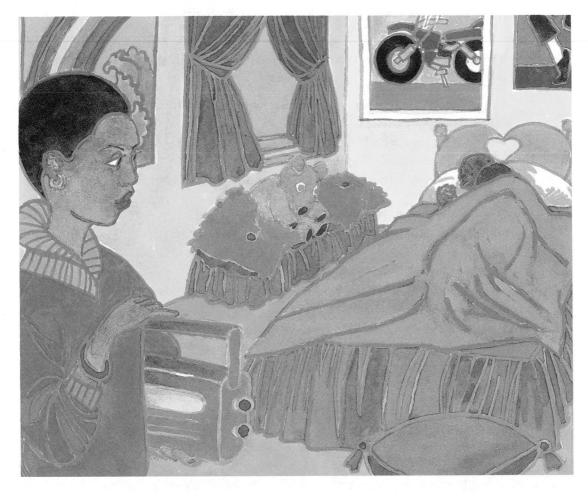

rights. But he understood. He knew how I felt.

"I just came in for this," I said, hurrying across the room to pick up my radio. My grandfather sat up for a moment and stared out my window. Then he fell back on the bed, as if in defeat.

"There's a park," I said slowly. "A few blocks away. It has trees."

As I closed the door, I heard him mumble. "I had that house for more than 40 years.

Don't even know the folks who own it now."

I stood outside the door, feeling confused. This day was filled with loss. I had lost my room, and I had lost my fight. Of course, my grandfather had lost something, too.

Tomorrow. Maybe tomorrow I would stand up for myself. Maybe then I would give him a hard time and make him leave.

Or maybe I would go out and buy some old-fashioned pictures for his room. ◆

READING CHECK

Answer the following questions about "A Private Place." You may want to check your answers by reviewing details in the story.

1. Why was Beth's grandfather coming to live with her family? Where did Beth think he should go instead?
2. What were two things Beth remembered about her grandparents' house and farm? Why did she stop going there long ago?
3. Whose room would Beth's grandfather move into? What did Beth think was unfair about that?
4. Why was Beth's mother angry at her after her grandfather came?
5. What did Beth plan to tell her grandfather when she walked into her room? What did she hope he would do then?
6. Why did Beth almost laugh when she saw her grandfather in her room? What did Granddad say that showed he understood her feelings about giving up her room?
7. At the end of the story, what did Beth decide to do for her grandfather?

WHAT DO YOU THINK

1. Why do you think Beth changed her mind about asking her grandfather to leave?
2. Beth lost her room to her grandfather. What do you think she gained?
3. If you had to give up your own room to an older relative and move in with a brother or sister, how would you handle the situation?

VOCABULARY CHECK

Read the following sentences and choose the correct meaning of each word in **bold print.** Then write each word and its meaning on your paper.

1. Beth tried not to let her expression turn into a **glare** when her grandfather came.
   (angry look, wide smile)
2. Beth's mother and father tried to make sure that Granddad did not feel like an **intruder.**
   (someone not smart, someone not invited)
3. Beth wondered what her grandfather would say if she **blurted** out her true feelings to him.
   (spoke suddenly, spoke softly)
4. It was easy to see the family **resemblance** when the father and grandfather stepped out of the car.
   (likeness, treasure)
5. Beth couldn't help feeling **impatient** with her sister, Jill.
   (grateful, annoyed)
6. It was not necessary for Beth to **barge** into her room.
   (enter silently, enter without warning)
7. Grandfather may have noticed the plastic **flamingo** on the grass.
   (large pink bird, lawn sprinkler)

STRATEGY CHECK

The paragraph below is based on the story "A Private Place." Choose a word that makes sense to fill in each blank. Use the rest of the parargaph and your knowledge of the story to help you. Then write the whole paragraph on your paper.

Beth felt lucky when she finally got her own ____. She got a ____ and earned enough money to buy curtains and pillows. She ____ the room bright yellow. Wild posters hung on the ____. This room was her own private ____, and it was important to her. When her grandfather moved in, she felt that she didn't ____ anywhere.

"AUNT SUSAN'S TRIAL"

In 1872, Susan B. Anthony was arrested and brought to trial. She had broken the law by voting in an election. A judge would decide whether she had actually committed the crime. This true story of Susan B. Anthony's trial is told by Harriot Stanton, a 16-year-old girl who lived during that exciting time.

WORDS TO KNOW

The words in **bold print** are from "Aunt Susan's Trial." Study each word and its meaning carefully.

Susan B. Anthony was taken to court by the deputy marshall since she refused to go **voluntarily.**
   voluntarily — willingly, of one's own free choice

Justice Ward Hunt **presided** over the courtroom in Susan's trial.
   presided — directed, was in charge of

Henry Seldon spoke **eloquently** about Susan B. Anthony's right to vote.
   eloquently — in a lively and forceful manner

Susan believed it was **vital** that she and all other women be allowed to vote.
   vital — very important

Susan only wanted to be treated fairly , and she asked the court for justice, not **leniency.**
   leniency — gentleness

Her voice rose in **defiance** as she urged all women to support her stand.
   defiance — bold resistance to authority

Judge Hunt was **unruffled** by the cheering in the courtroom and went on to give his decision.
   unruffled — not disturbed

AUNT SUSAN'S TRIAL

by WILLIAM JAY JACOBS

My name is Harriot Stanton. My mother's name is Elizabeth Cady Stanton. She is known throughout the United States for her fight to get the same rights for women that men already have. Mother's best friend is Susan B. Anthony. Even though Susan is not related to us, she is almost a part of the family. So, we call her Aunt Susan.

In 1848, eight years before I was born, Mother and a small group of other ladies announced a women's rights meeting in Seneca Falls, New York. Mother wrote a Declaration of Sentiments that was similar to the Declaration of Independence written by Thomas Jefferson in 1776. But instead of just saying "All men were created equal," Mother's declaration said "All men AND WOMEN were created equal."

Since 1848, the year of the Seneca Falls Convention, men had been saying to women, "No! No! No! You can't vote!" Well, Susan B. Anthony decided to do something direct and simple to change the situation.

She voted.

It all started when Virginia Minor, a friend of Mother's, said to Susan, "After all, you are a citizen, aren't you? If you tried to vote and they let you, they couldn't stop other women. And if they stopped you, just imagine how angry that would make the female population of this country!"

"Not letting you vote," said Mrs. Minor, "would mean you'd be less of a citizen than every newly freed slave. So would every man's mother, wife, sister, and daughter. Women just wouldn't stand for that. They'd be fighting mad."

So, in the Presidential election of 1872, along with 15 other women, Susan B.

Anthony walked into the polling place in Rochester, New York, and voted.

Here's part of the letter she wrote to Mother that day:

Well, I have gone and done it, positively voted this morning at 7 o'clock. . . . Not a jeer, not a rude word, not a disrespectful look has met one woman [with me]. . . . I'm so tired! I've been on the go constantly for five days, but to good purpose, so all right.

Then the police stepped in. About two weeks after the election, a deputy United States marshal, blushing and stuttering, appeared at Susan's house. He announced that it was his duty to arrest her. It was against the law for a woman to vote, he said. She had committed a crime.

He asked her to present herself in court.

"Oh, no," she said. "I shall not go there voluntarily. In fact, I would like you to handcuff me and take me there."

The deputy refused to handcuff Susan, but he did take her to court. She was questioned and a date was set for her trial — June 17, 1873.

Even with her trial coming up, Susan continued her lecture tour, speaking on important topics. One of her new topics was: "Is it a crime for a United States citizen to vote?" That's what the trial was to decide.

On the day of the trial the courtroom was packed. People had come from all over the country. A former President of the United States, Millard Fillmore, was in the audience. Newspapermen crowded the aisles. Susan and the other women who had voted on Election Day were seated behind the prisoners' bar.

Justice Ward Hunt presided as trial judge. Henry B. Selden served as Susan B. Anthony's chief attorney. Mr. Selden said that when Susan voted, she thought she had a right to vote. So, what she did could not be considered a crime. She was putting her idea to a test. Moreover, women legally *did* have the right to vote, he said, according to the Constitution.

Mr. Selden's speech was clear, logical, and to the point. For more than three hours, he spoke eloquently.

But Judge Hunt hardly listened at all. Instead, he read a statement that he had prepared before coming into court — before he had heard the argument for the defense.

Then he ordered the all-male jury to find Susan B. Anthony guilty as charged.

Mr. Selden jumped to his feet. "I object! I object!" he shouted. "No judge has a right in a criminal case to tell a jury what to decide. I demand that the members of the jury be allowed to vote."

But Judge Hunt dismissed the jury without letting one of its members speak.

The next day, Susan's lawyers asked for a new trial. Judge Hunt turned down the request. He then ordered Susan to stand for sentencing. "Has the prisoner anything to say on why sentence shall not be pronounced?" asked Judge Hunt.

Susan, dressed in black except for a trimming of white lace at her neckline,

paused for an instant. Then she spoke firmly and forcefully.

"Yes, Your Honor, I have many things to say, for in your ordered verdict of guilty you have trampled under foot every vital principle of our government. My natural rights, my civil rights, my political rights, my judicial rights are all alike ignored."

Judge Hunt, impatient, interrupted. Pointing at the accused, he declared, "The Court cannot allow the prisoner to go on."

But Susan would not stop. Since the day of her arrest, she had been given no chance to defend herself. Judge Hunt had not even allowed her to be a witness for herself at the trial.

"The prisoner must sit down — the Court cannot allow it," bellowed Judge Hunt.

Susan continued: "Had Your Honor submitted my case to the jury, as was clearly your duty, even then I should have had just cause of protest, for not one of those men was my peer; but native or foreign-born, rich or poor, educated or ignorant, sober or drunk, each and every man of them was my political superior. . . . Under such circumstances a commoner in England, tried before a jury of lords, would have far less cause to complain than have I, a woman, tried before a jury of men."

"The Court must insist," Judge Hunt interrupted again. "The prisoner has been tried according to the established forms of the law."

"Yes, Your Honor," answered Susan, "but by forms of law all made by men, interpreted by men, in favor of men, and against women."

"The Court orders the prisoner to sit down. It will not allow another word!" shouted Judge Hunt, banging his gavel for order.

Susan had a final word. She had expected, she said, a fair trial and justice. "But failing to get this justice . . . I ask not leniency at your hands but rather the full rigor of the law."

"The Court must insist . . ." started Judge Hunt. At that point Susan sat down.

"The prisoner will stand up," directed the judge.

Again she rose.

"The sentence of the Court is that you pay a fine of 100 dollars and the costs of prosecution."

"May it please Your Honor," began Susan. "I will never pay a dollar of your unjust penalty. All I possess is a debt of 10,000 dollars incurred by publishing my paper — *The Revolution* — the sole object of which was to educate all women to do precisely as I have done: rebel against your man-made, unjust, unconstitutional forms of law, which tax, fine, imprison, and hang women, while denying them the right of representation in the government."

Susan, remaining calm, but with her voice rising in defiance, then concluded: "I will work on with might and main to pay every dollar of that honest debt, but not a penny shall go to this unjust claim. And I shall earnestly and persistently continue to urge all women to the practical recognition of the old Revolutionary maxim, 'Resistance to tyranny is obedience to God.' "

For a moment, the courtroom was hushed in silence. Later, we heard that even some members of the jury said they had felt like applauding, perhaps even cheering out loud.

Judge Hunt, unruffled, proceeded. Since Susan B. Anthony refused to pay the $100 fine, he could have her sent to jail. But then she would have had the right to appeal her case to the United States Supreme Court. Instead, he said, "Madam, the Court will not order you to stand committed until the fine is paid."

That meant he would not send her to jail.

And, of course, Susan never paid the fine.

My mother often speaks and writes about Susan's trial. She compares it to something else that happened on June 17 nearly a century ago — the Battle of Bunker Hill in the American Revolution. In that battle the American Colonists were forced back, almost wiped out. But they kept on fighting. They lost the battle. But they won the war, and won their freedom from Great Britain.

Mother likes to think that some day — maybe a century from now — people will look back on Susan B. Anthony's trial and remember her as a hero — a hero in the struggle to win equal rights for women. ◆

READING CHECK

Answer the following questions about "Aunt Susan's Trial." You may want to check your answers by reviewing details in the story.

1. What action did Susan B. Anthony take in the Presidential election of 1872? Why was her action unusual?

2. Why was Susan B. Anthony arrested two weeks after the election? Where was she taken?

3. What two main points did Henry B. Seldon make in his defense of Susan during her trial?

4. What did Judge Hunt order the jury to do? Why did Mr. Seldon object? What did Judge Hunt do then?

5. Why did Susan insist on speaking when Judge Hunt tried to stop her?

6. What was Judge Hunt's sentence at the end of the trial?

7. Why did Susan refuse to pay the fine? How did her refusal to pay the fine keep her out of jail?

WHAT DO YOU THINK?

1. Do you think Susan B. Anthony's trial was fair? Explain.

2. In what way could it be said that Susan B. Anthony "lost the battle but won the war," in her struggle for equal rights for women?

3. Do you consider Susan B. Anthony a hero? Why, or why not?

VOCABULARY CHECK

Read the following sentences and choose the correct meaning of each word in **bold print.** Then write each word and its meaning on your paper.

1. Susan told Judge Hunt that she would not **voluntarily** pay his fine.
   (willingly, happily)

2. Susan spoke so **eloquently** that the members of the jury almost cheered.
   (humorously, forcefully)

3. The accused was **unruffled** when the judge told her to stop speaking.
   (not disturbed, not amused)

4. Refusing to accept the orders of the judge was an act of **defiance** by Susan.
   (resistance, sorrow)

5. Susan dreamed of the day a courtroom could be **presided** over by a woman.
   (directed, prepared)

6. It was **vital** to women's rights that Susan defend herself in court.
   (important, hopeful)

7. No woman on trial for voting in 1872 could expect **leniency** from the court.
   (praise, gentleness)

STRATEGY CHECK

The paragraph below is based on "Aunt Susan's Trial." Choose a word that makes sense to fill in each blank. Use the rest of the paragraph and your knowledge of the story to help you. Then write the whole paragrah on your paper.

In 1872, Susan B. Anthony walked into a polling place in Rochester, New York, and ___. Two weeks after the election, she was arrested and charged with a ___. It was against the ___ for women to vote. Susan's ___ began on June 17. The judge did not want the prisoner to ___ in the courtroom. But Susan insisted on defending the rights of ___ to do exactly as men were allowed to do in an election.

◆ INTRODUCING ◆

"AMIGO BROTHERS"

What will happen when two best friends meet in the boxing ring? Both are determined to win, and both know that there can be only one winner. In this case, winning means not only beating a best friend, but maybe hurting him, too. Find out how Antonio and Felix meet the greatest challenge of their lives in this exciting story.

WORDS TO KNOW

The words in **bold print** are from "Amigo Brothers." Study each word and its meaning carefully.

Antonio was lean and **lanky,** and had a long reach.
  lanky — tall and thin

Felix was shorter than Antonio, but more **muscular.**
  muscular — powerful

The two friends met in the ring many times for short **sparring** sessions.
  sparring — boxing practice

The sounds of cars **mingled** with the laughter of children in the street.
  mingled — mixed together

A dozen of Felix's fans **escorted** him to the ring.
  escorted — accompanied, went along with

The boxers' robes were lifted from their shoulders by their trainers' **nimble** fingers.
  nimble — quick and light

Antonio and Felix **embraced** and shook hands before the fight.
  embraced — hugged

AMIGO BROTHERS

by PIRI THOMAS

Antonio Cruz and Felix Varga were both 17 years old. They were so close in friendship that they felt themselves to be brothers. All of their lives, they had lived on the lower east side of Manhattan, in the same building.

Antonio was fair, lean, and lanky, while Felix was dark, short, and husky. Antonio's hair was always falling over his eyes, while Felix wore his curly black hair short.

Each had a dream of someday becoming lightweight champion of the world. Every chance they had, the boys worked out. Sometimes they went to the Boys Club. Sometimes they went to the pro's gym. Early morning sunrises would find them running along the East River Drive, wearing sweat shirts, short towels around their necks, and handkerchiefs around their foreheads.

Each had fought many bouts representing their community and had won medals. The difference between them was in their styles. Antonio's lean form and long reach made him the better boxer, while Felix's short and muscular frame made him the better slugger. Whenever they had met in the ring for sparring sessions, it had always been hot and heavy.

Now, after a series of elimination bouts, they had been informed that they were to meet each other in the division finals. The finals were scheduled for the seventh of August, two weeks away. The winner would represent the Boys Club in the Golden Gloves Championship Tournament.

The two boys continued to run together along the East River Drive. But even when joking with each other, they both sensed a wall rising between them.

One morning, less than a week before their bout, they met as usual for their daily work-out. They fooled around with a few jabs at the air. Then they took off, running lightly along the East River's edge.

Antonio glanced at Felix. But Felix kept

his eyes straight ahead. He stopped from time to time to do some fancy legwork and throw upper cuts to an imaginary jaw. Antonio then beat the air with a number of body blows and short, hard lefts and an overhand jaw-breaking right.

After a mile or so, Felix puffed and said, "Let's stop a while, brother. I think we both got something to say to each other."

Antonio nodded. It was not natural to be acting as though nothing unusual was happening. Two best friends were going· to be fighting each other within a few short days.

They rested their elbows on the railing separating them from the river. Antonio wiped his face with his short towel. The sunrise was now creating day.

Felix leaned heavily on the river's railing. He stared across to the shores of Brooklyn. Finally, he broke the silence.

"Man, I don't know how to say it."

Antonio helped. "It's our fight, right?"

"Yeah, right." Felix's eyes squinted at the rising orange sun.

"I've been thinking about it, too. In fact, since we found out it was going to be me and you, I've been awake at night. I think about pulling punches on you, trying not to hurt you."

"Same here. It isn't natural not to think about the fight. I mean, we both are *fighters* and we both want to win. But only one of us can win. There are no draws in the eliminations."

Felix tapped Antonio gently on the shoulder. "I don't mean to sound like I'm bragging, but I want to win, fair and square."

Antonio nodded quietly. "Yeah. We both know that in the ring the better fighter wins. Friend or no friend, brother or no . . ."

Felix finished it for him. "Brother. Tony, let's promise something right here. Okay?"

"If it's fair, I'm for it."

"It's fair, Tony. When we get into the ring, it's got to be like we never met. We have to be like two strangers that want the same thing and only one can have it. You understand, don't you?"

"Yeah, I know." Tony smiled. "No pulling punches. We go all the way."

"Yeah, that's right. Listen, Tony. Don't you think it's a good idea if we don't see each other until the day of the fight? I'm going to stay with my Aunt Lucy in the Bronx. I can use Gleason's Gym for working out. My manager says he got some sparring partners with more or less your style."

Tony scratched his nose thoughtfully. "Yeah, it would be better." He held out his hand, palm upward. "Deal?"

"Deal." Felix lightly slapped open skin.

"Ready for some more running?" Tony asked awkwardly.

"Naw, brother. Let's cut it here. You go on. I'd like to get things together in my head."

"You're not worried, are you?" Tony asked.

"No way, man." Felix laughed out loud. "I just think it's cooler if we split right here. After the fight, we can get it together again. It will be as if nothing ever happened."

The *amigo* brothers were not ashamed to hug each other tightly.

"Guess you're right. Watch yourself up in the Bronx, Felix, okay?"

"Okay. You watch yourself, too."

Tony jogged away. Felix watched his friend disappear from view, throwing rights and lefts. Both fighters had a lot of preparation before the big fight.

The evening before the big fight, Tony made his way to the roof of his building. In the quiet, early dark, he peered over the ledge. Six stories below, the lights of the city blinked and the sounds of cars mingled with the laughter of children in the street. He tried not to think of Felix. He felt he could win. But only in the ring would he really know. To spare Felix hurt, he would have to knock him out, early and quickly.

Up in the South Bronx, Felix went to see the movie *The Champion* and thought about keeping Antonio's face away from his fists.

In the movie, the champion was getting badly beaten. His face was being pounded into raw, wet hamburger. His eyes were cut. One eye was swollen, the other almost shut. He was saved only by the sound of the bell.

Felix became the champ and Tony the challenger.

Felix's right arm felt the shock. He imagined Antonio's face, on the screen, shattered by the awesome force of the blow.

Felix saw himself in the ring. He was blasting Antonio against the ropes. The champ had to be restrained by the referee. The challenger was allowed to crumble slowly to the canvas.

When Felix finally left the theater, he had figured out how to prepare himself for tomorrow's fight. It was Felix the Champion vs. Antonio the Challenger.

The fight was scheduled to take place in Tompkins Square Park. It had been decided that the Boys Club gym was not large enough to hold all the people who were sure to attend. In Tompkins Square Park, everyone who wanted to could view the fight. People could watch from ringside, or windows, or rooftops.

The morning of the fight, Tompkins Square was a beehive of activity. Workers set up the ring, the seats, and the guest speakers' stand. The scheduled bouts began shortly after noon, and the park had begun filling up even earlier.

The local junior high school, across from Tompkins Square Park, was used as the dressing room for all the fighters. Each was given a separate classroom. Antonio thought he caught a glimpse of Felix waving to him from a room at the far end of the hall. He waved back just in case it had been Felix.

The fighters changed from their street clothes into fighting gear. Antonio wore white trunks, black socks, and black shoes. Felix wore sky-blue trunks, red socks, and white boxing shoes. Each had a robe to

match his fighting trunks with his name neatly stitched on the back.

After the sixth bout, Felix's trainer, Charlie, said, "This is it. We're on."

Waiting time was over. Felix was escorted from the classroom by a dozen fans. All the fans wore white T-shirts with the word FELIX across their fronts.

Antonio was escorted down a different stairwell and guided through a roped-off path.

As the two climbed into the ring, the crowd roared. Antonio and Felix both bowed gracefully and then raised their arms to the crowd.

Antonio tried to be cool. He turned slowly to meet Felix's eyes looking directly into his. Felix nodded his head and Antonio responded. And each fighter quickly turned away to face his own corner.

Bong! Bong! Bong! The roar of the crowd turned to stillness.

"Ladies and gentlemen, now the moment we have all been waiting for — the main event between two fine young Puerto Rican fighters, from the Lower East Side. In this corner, weighing 134 pounds, Felix Vargas. And in this corner, weighing 133 pounds, Antonio Cruz. The winner will represent the Boys Club in the tournament of champions, the Golden Gloves. There will be no draw. May the best man win."

The cheering of the crowd shook the windowpanes of the old buildings surrounding Tompkins Square Park. At the center of the ring, the referee was giving instructions to the fighters.

"Keep your punches up. No low blows. No punching on the back of the head. Keep your heads up. Understand? Let's have a clean fight. Now shake hands and come out fighting."

Both fighters touched gloves and nodded. They turned and danced quickly to their corners. Their towels and robes were lifted neatly from their shoulders by their trainers' nimble fingers.

Bong! Bong! Round one. Felix and Antonio turned and faced each other squarely in a fighting pose. Felix wasted no time. He came in fast. He held his head low. Then he half hunched toward his right shoulder, and lashed out with a straight left. Antonio slipped the punch and countered with three lefts that snapped Felix's head back. If Felix had any doubts about their friendship affecting their fight, those doubts were now gone.

Antonio danced, a joy to behold. His left hand pumped jabs one right after another. Felix bobbed and weaved. He knew that at long range he was at a disadvantage. Antonio had too much reach on him. Only by coming in close could Felix hope to achieve the dreamed-of knockout.

Antonio knew the dynamite that was stored in his *amigo* brother's fist. He ducked a short right and missed a left hook. Felix trapped him against the ropes, but Antonio slipped away from Felix. The match went

on. Each fighter threw punches and felt the force of the other's blows.

Bong! Both *amigos* froze a punch well on its way, sending up a roar of approval for good sportsmanship.

Felix walked briskly back to his corner. His right ear had not stopped ringing from Antonio's last punch. Antonio gracefully danced his way toward his stool. He felt fine except for glowing glove burns, showing angry red against his midribs.

"Watch that right, Tony." His trainer talked into his ear. "Remember, Felix always goes to the body."

Felix's corner was also busy.

"You got to get in there, fella." Felix's trainer poured water over his curly hair. "Get in there or he's going to chop you up from way back."

Bong! Bong! Round two. Felix was off his stool. He rushed Antonio like a bull, sending a hard right to his head. Beads of water exploded from Antonio's long hair.

Antonio moved in too close and Felix tangled him up in a rip-roaring exchange of blows.

Rights to the body. Lefts to the head. Neither fighter gave an inch. Suddenly a short right caught Antonio squarely on the chin. His long legs turned to jelly. His arms flailed out desperately. Felix, grunting like a bull, threw wild punches from every direction. Antonio was groggy. He bobbed and weaved and avoided most of the blows. Suddenly, his head cleared. His left flashed out hard and straight, catching Felix on the bridge of his nose.

Felix lashed back with a right. At the same instant, his eye caught another left hook from Antonio. Felix swung out, trying to clear the pain. Only the screaming of the crowd let him know that he had knocked Antonio down.

Antonio struggled to his feet and threw a smashing right that dropped Felix flat on his back. His head cleared to hear the bell sound at the end of the round. He was glad. His trainer sat him down on the stool.

In his corner, Antonio was doing what all fighters do when they are hurt. They sit and smile at everyone.

The referee signaled the ring doctor to check the fighters out. He did so. Then he gave his okay. The cold water sponges refreshed both *amigo* brothers.

Bong! Round three — the final round. Up to now it had been even. But everyone knew there could be no draw. This round would decide the winner.

This time, to Felix's surprise, it was Antonio who came out fast. Antonio charged across the ring. Felix braced himself, but couldn't ward off the punches. Antonio drove Felix hard against the ropes.

Felix tapped his gloves. Then he began his attack anew.

Both pounded away. Neither gave an inch. Felix's left eye was tightly closed. Blood poured from Antonio's nose.

Bong! Bong! Bong! The bell sounded over and over again. Felix and Antonio were past hearing. Their blows continued to pound on each other like hammers.

Finally the referee and the two trainers pulled Felix and Antonio apart. Cold water was poured over them to bring them back to their senses.

They looked around. Then they rushed toward each other. A cry of alarm went through the park. Was this a fight to the death instead of a boxing match?

The fear soon gave way to cheering as the two *amigos* embraced.

No matter what the decision, they knew they would always be champions to each other.

Bong! Bong! Bong! "Ladies and gentlemen, the winner and representative to the Golden Gloves Tournament of Champions is . . . "

The announcer turned to point to the winner. But he found himself alone. Arm in arm, the champions had already left the ring. ◆

READING CHECK

Answer the following questions about "Amigo Brothers." You may want to check your answers by reviewing details in the story.

1. What dream did Antonio and Felix have for the future? How did they stay in shape?

2. What boxing event was planned for the seventh of August? What contest would the winner then take part in?

3. What did Felix and Antonio promise each other when they were out running?

4. Where did Antonio go the night before the fight? What did he decide to do? Where did Felix go? What did he decide about the next day's fight?

5. Where did the division finals take place? Why did the crowd roar its approval at the end of the first round?

6. Why did the referee and the trainers have to pull Felix and Antonio apart after the final round was over?

7. Where were the two boxers when the winner was announced?

WHAT DO YOU THINK?

1. Why do you think Felix and Antonio left the ring before the winner was announced?

2. How would you feel about competing in a contest with a close friend? What would you say to your friend if you won, or if you lost?

3. Do you think that boxing helps to promote good sportsmanship in young people? Give reasons for your answer.

VOCABULARY CHECK

Read the following sentences and choose the correct meaning of each word in **bold print.** Then write each word and its meaning on your paper.

1. Both fighters had **nimble** feet as they danced in the ring.
   (quick, rough)

2. Antonio's **lanky** build gave him the advantage of a long reach against Felix.
   (straight and firm, tall and thin)

3. The crowd could see that Felix was more **muscular** than Antonio.
   (hot-tempered, powerful)

4. Felix's trainer had set up some **sparring** partners for him before the fight.
   (practice, lucky)

5. Both boxers were **escorted** to the ring by their fans.
   (accompanied, cheered)

6. The sounds of the crowd **mingled** with the voice of the referee.
   (moved, mixed)

7. Antonio and Felix **embraced** and promised that they would always be champions to each other.
   (clapped, hugged)

STRATEGY CHECK

The paragraph below is based on the story "Amigo Brothers." Choose a word that makes sense to fill in each blank. Use the rest of the paragraph and your knowledge of the story to help you. Then write the whole paragraph on your paper.

   Both Felix and Antonio ____ of becoming the lightweight boxing champion of the world. They ____ out whenever they had free time. In the early morning, they ran along the ____. Both had _____ many bouts, representing their community. Both Antonio and Felix ____ to be the winner of the division finals, but there could be only one winner.

"POEMS ABOUT WINNING AND LOSING"

The poems that you will read here bring to life the feelings that athletes experience during an important meet or race. Although you may never have pole vaulted, or even run a race, you may find that the feelings described here are not unlike your own feelings when you find yourself up at bat or ready to do your best at some competitive event.

WORDS TO KNOW

The words in **bold print** are from "Poems About Winning and Losing." Study each word and it's meaning carefully.

The pole vaulter was **ascending** into the air.
    ascending — rising

His **descent** was quick and he hit the ground hard.
    descent — downward movement, fall

At the starting line, the runners were **skittish.**
    skittish — lively but nervous or careful

They **flex** their knees back and forth to move their legs.
    flex — bend

They went **careening** off from their starting blocks.
    careening — tilting, lurching

THE WOMEN'S 400 METERS

by LILLIAN MORRISON

Skittish,
they flex knees, drum
    heels and
shiver at the starting
    line

waiting the gun
to pour them over the
    stretch
like a breaking wave.

Bang! they're off
careening down the
    lanes,
each chased by her own
    bright tiger.

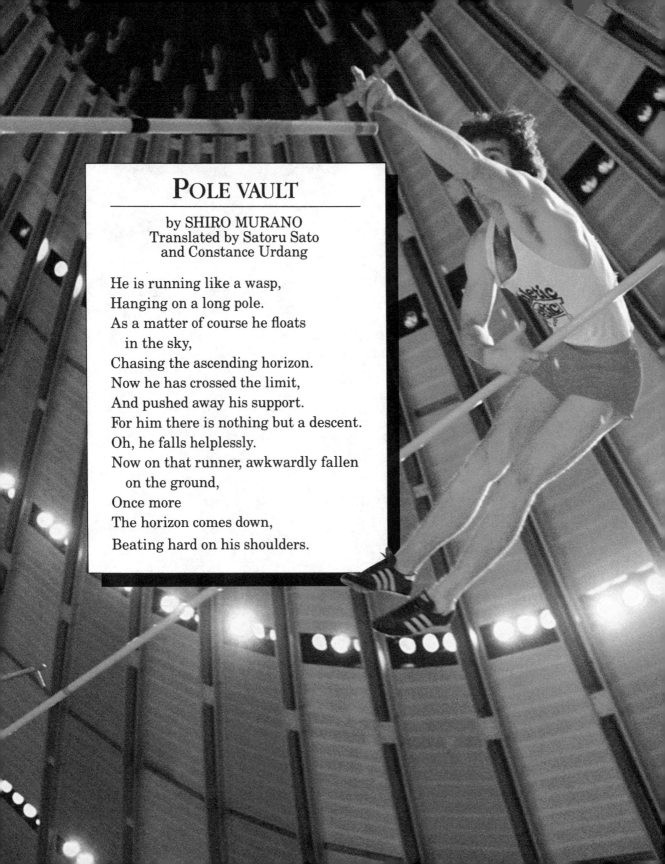

POLE VAULT

by SHIRO MURANO
Translated by Satoru Sato
and Constance Urdang

He is running like a wasp,
Hanging on a long pole.
As a matter of course he floats
   in the sky,
Chasing the ascending horizon.
Now he has crossed the limit,
And pushed away his support.
For him there is nothing but a descent.
Oh, he falls helplessly.
Now on that runner, awkwardly fallen
   on the ground,
Once more
The horizon comes down,
Beating hard on his shoulders.

WHAT DO YOU THINK?

1. Think about how a pole vaulter moves up and over the bar and then lands on the mat. Look at the details in the poem "Pole Vault." What do you think that the person described in the poem liked best about pole vaulting: rising up over the bar, or landing on the ground?

2. In "The Women's 400 Meters," how do the runners feel before the race actually begins? Use lines from the poem to explain your answer.

3. What do you think that Lillian Morrison means when she says that each runner is "chased by her own bright tiger"?

4. Both "Pole Vault" and "The Women's 400 Meters" describe how athletes move and feel during an event. Which poem do you think gives a clearer picture of how the athlete moves and feels? Explain your answer.

VOCABULARY CHECK

Read the following sentences and choose the correct meaning of each word in **bold print.** Then write each word and its meaning on your paper.

1. The racers came **careening** towards the finish line.
     (tilting or lurching, strolling or limping)

2. **Flex** your knees before you get ready to jump.
     (bandage, bend)

3. After being up so high, the **descent** to the ground seemed to come all too quickly.
     (race, fall)

4. The athlete's training prepared him for **ascending** high above the stick.
     (exercising, rising)

5. She felt **skittish** as she waited for the race to begin.
     (lively, bored)

◆ UNIT REVIEW ◆

READING REVIEW

Winning and Losing is about people who win, even when they sometimes seem to lose. Complete a sentence about each selection in the unit. Choose the best ending for each sentence. Then write the complete sentences on your paper.

1. In "The Grand Prize," Mitchell's parents did not believe he would ever ___.
   a. get along with Lynda
   b. teach his parrot to talk
   c. win a sweepstakes contest
   d. buy his own stamps

2. Mitchell's parrot, Dennis, stole the show in front of the television cameras when he ___.
   a. sat on Mitchell's shoulder
   b. said the name of the product
   c. chewed on a check
   d. escaped from his cage

3. In "A Private Place," the reason for Beth's anger was ___.
   a. the loss of her room
   b. her grandfather's pictures
   c. her sister's complaints
   d. the rain that never stopped

4. In "Aunt Susan's Trial," Susan B. Anthony was arrested and charged with a crime because she ___.
   a. broke the speed limit
   b. argued with a judge
   c. refused a trial
   d. voted in an election

5. Susan B. Anthony was most upset at her trial by ___.
   a. the anger of the judge
   b. the unfairness of the law
   c. the amount of her fine
   d. the arguments of her lawyers

6. At the end of "Amigo Brothers," Felix and Antonio walked away from the ring arm and arm because they ___.
   a. hoped for a tie
   b. were badly injured
   c. remained close friends
   d. both won medals

VOCABULARY REVIEW

Review some words about winning and losing. Choose a word from the list to replace the words in **bold print** in each sentence below. Then write the completed sentences on your paper.

limousine	**ceremony**	**deserted**
penalty	**tournament**	**challenger**

1. When the contest was over a **formal event** was held to honor all the winners.

2. The one who scores the most points in the **series of contests** will win.

3. A ride in a **large, fancy automobile** is one of the prizes in the contest.

4. Today, no one is asked to pay a **fine** for exercising the right to vote.

5. The mayor will run against **someone who wants his job** in the next election.

6. The two friends had not **left** one another; they had become closer than ever.

WRITING ABOUT
WINNING AND LOSING

1. "The Grand Prize" is a humorous story about an unlikely event — the winning of a huge sum of money. Write your own humorous short story about winning a different kind of grand prize, such as an enormous pet, an airplane, or a whole island. If you prefer not to write about yourself as the prize winner, invent a character whose life changes as a result of sudden good fortune.

2. In "A Private Place," Beth and her grandfather seem to develop some understanding between them. Think of some ways in which young people and old people (not necessarily relatives) can share their interests. Make a list of some activities that could bring young and old together to increase understanding between the groups. (One example: a pen pal program between young students and residents of a home for the aged.) Use your list as the basis of a letter to community organizations or a local newspaper.

UNIT
·6·

TIGHT SPOTS

Have you ever been in a tight spot — the kind of situation where you need all of your wits, and even a bit of luck, to pull through? The selection in this unit are all about people who find themselves in tough spots.

In "He Was a Good Lion," Beryl has a surprise encounter with a lion everyone had thought was tame. In "Buried Treasure," Speed Armstrong teases Brian and Pat and their dog Clarence, but in the end depends on them to get out of trouble. In "The Thinking Machine," Professor Van Dusen has himself locked up in prison to show that he can *think* his way out of any tight spot.

The poems "A Narrow Fellow in the Grass" and "The Shark" are about mysterious and dangerous creatures. "Be Like the Bird" is about a bird finding himself in trouble in mid-flight.

When you're in a tight spot, you might think and act more quickly than you thought you could. Tight spots may be frightening — even dangerous — but they often bring out the best in you.

UNDERSTANDING WORDS IN SENTENCES

Words That Describe Situations. Five words that describe situations or people in situations are in **bold print** below. Each of the words is used in *Tight Spots*. Use the sentence pairs to help you find the correct meaning of the words in **bold print.** Write the word and its meaning on your paper.

1. The crab **scuttled** forward. Clarence ran after it.
    (ran quickly and jerkily, dug a deep hole)

2. The Elkington lion was **suspicious** of his equals. But he could always be trusted to be exactly what he was.
    (not trusting, not hungry)

3. Beryl **nudged** her horse. Then the horse broke into a run.
    (pulled hard, pushed gently)

4. The prison officials had all heard of Professor Van Dusen. He would be their most **distinguished** prisoner.
    (famous, intelligent)

5. The professor **squinted** at the light. Then he traced the wire leading to it.
    (yelled at the top of his lungs, looked with slightly closed eyes)

"HE WAS A GOOD LION"

Beryl Markham grew up in Africa early in the 1900 s. In this true story, she tells about one of her experiences, where she comes face to face with a lion.

WORDS TO KNOW

The words in **bold print** are from "He Was a Good Lion." Study each word and its meaning carefully.

Beryl's father told her that lions were **contemptuous** of cowards.
   contemptuous — without respect for

Their **destination** was Elkington's farm.
   destination — specific place one travels to, or wants to reach

Bishon Singh greeted Beryl in **Swahili.**
   Swahili — a language spoken in Africa

The lion lay **sprawled** in the morning sun.
   sprawled — stretched out

No one had thought of Paddy as holding any **menace.**
   menace — threat of danger

Bishon Singh believed one **circumstance** saved Beryl's life.
   circumstance — event or happening

Beryl could not **begrudge** Paddy his right to act like a wild lion.
   begrudge — resent someone for, be angry with

HE WAS
A GOOD LION

by BERYL MARKHAM

When I was a child, in the early 1900s, I moved to East Africa with my father, who was a horse breeder and farmer.

There was a place called Elkington's Farm near Nairobi, on the edge of the Kikuyu Reserve. My father and I used to ride there from town on horses or in a buggy. As we rode along the way, my father would tell me things about Africa.

Sometimes he would tell me stories about the great tribal leaders and their way of life which, to me, seemed much greater fun than our own.

He would tell me old legends sometimes about Mount Kenya, or about Mount Kilimanjaro. He would tell me these things and I would ride alongside and ask endless questions, or we would sit together in the jolting buggy and just think about what he had said.

One day, when we were riding to Elkington's, my father spoke about lions.

"Lions are more intelligent than some people," he said, "and braver than most. A lion will fight for what he has and for what he needs; he is contemptuous of cowards. And he is suspicious of his equals. But he is not afraid. You can always trust a lion to be exactly what he is — and never anything else."

"Except, Beryl," he added, looking more fatherly and concerned than usual, "that lion of Elkington's!"

The Elkington lion was famous within a radius of 12 miles in all directions from the farm. If you happened to be anywhere inside that circle, you could hear him roar.

He roared when he was hungry, when he was sad, or when he just felt like roaring.

Two or three of the English settlers in East Africa at that time had caught lion cubs and raised them in cages. But Paddy, the Elkington lion, had never seen a cage.

He had grown to full size, without a worry or a care. He lived on fresh meat, not of his own killing. He spent his waking hours (everybody else's sleeping hours) wandering through Elkington's fields and pastures like an emperor strolling in the gardens of his court.

He liked solitude. He had no mate, but pretended not to care and walked alone. There were no physical barriers to his freedom, but the lions of the plains do not accept any lion with the smell of men on his coat. So Paddy ate, slept, and roared, and perhaps he sometimes dreamed, but he never left Elkington's. He was a tame lion, Paddy was. He was deaf to the call of the wild.

"I'm always careful of that lion," I told my father, "but he's really harmless. I have seen Mrs. Elkington stroke him."

"Which proves nothing," said my father. "A tamed lion is only an unnatural lion — and whatever is unnatural is untrustworthy."

Whenever my father made an observation like that one, I knew there was nothing more to be said.

I nudged my horse and we broke into a canter. It was not long before we arrived at Elkington's farm.

It wasn't a big farm as farms went in Africa before the First World War, but it had a very nice house with a large porch. My father, Jim Elkington, Mrs. Elkington, and one or two other settlers sat on the porch and talked.

There was a tea table lavishly spread, as only the English can spread them.

But cakes and muffins were no fit bribery for me. I had pleasures of my own then, or constant expectations. I said a few polite words. Then I left the house.

As I scampered past the square hay shed behind the Elkington house, I caught sight of Bishon Singh. He was from India, and he worked on my father's farm. My father had sent him ahead to tend our horses.

He raised his arm and greeted me in Swahili as I ran through the Elkington farmyard and out toward the open country. I had no specific destination in mind. But I always ran as fast as I could in the hope of finding one — and I always found it.

I was within 20 yards of the Elkington lion before I saw him. He lay sprawled in the morning sun. He was huge, black-maned, and gleaming with life. His tail moved slowly, stroking the rough grass like a knotted rope end. His body was sleek and easy, making a mold where he lay, a cool mold that would be there when he had gone. He was not asleep; he was only idle. He was rusty-red, and soft, like a strokable cat.

I stopped. And he lifted his head with magnificent ease. Then he stared at me out of yellow eyes.

I stood there staring back, scuffling my bare toes in the dust, pursing my lips to make a noiseless whistle — a very small girl who knew about lions.

Paddy raised himself. Giving a little sigh, he began to look at me carefully and quietly.

I cannot say that there was any menace in his eyes, because there wasn't. I cannot say his "frightful jowls" were drooling, because they were handsome jowls and very tidy. He did sniff the air, though, in a satisfied manner, I thought. And he did not lie down again.

I remembered the rules that one remembers. I did not run. I walked very slowly, and I began to sing a defiant song I had learned in Africa.

"Kali coma Simba sisi," I sang, *"Asikari yoti ni udari!* — Fierce like the lion are we, *Asikari* all are brave!"

I went in a straight line past Paddy when I sang it. I saw his eyes shine in the thick grass. I watched his tail beat time to the meter of my song.

"Twendi, twendi—ku pigana—piga aduoi— piga sana! — Let us go, let us go — to fight — beat down the enemy! Beat hard, beat hard!"

What lion would be unimpressed with the marching song of the King's African Rifles?

Singing it still, I took up my trot toward the rim of the low hill. There, if I was lucky, I'd find gooseberry bushes to hide behind.

The country was gray-green and dry, and the sun lay on it closely, making the ground hot under my bare feet. There was no sound and no wind.

Even Paddy made no sound, coming swiftly behind me.

What I remember most clearly of the moment that followed are three things. First, I heard a scream that was barely a whisper. Second, I felt a blow that struck me to the ground. Then third, as I buried my face in my arms and felt Paddy's teeth

close on the flesh of my leg, I saw a fantastically bobbing turban. That was Bishon Singh's turban appearing over the edge of the hill.

I remained conscious, but I closed my eyes and tried not to be. It was not so much the pain as it was the sound — the sound of Paddy's roar in my ears.

I shut my eyes very tight. I lay still under the weight of Paddy's paws.

Bishon Singh said afterward that he did nothing. He said he had remained by the hay shed for a few minutes after I ran past him. But then, for no explainable reason, he had begun to follow me. He admitted, though, that, a little while before, he had seen Paddy go in the direction I had taken.

Singh called for help, of course, when he saw the lion meant to attack. A half-dozen of Elkington's workers had come running from the house. Along with them had come Jim Elkington with a rawhide whip.

Jim Elkington was one of those enormous men whose girth alone seemed to rule out any possibility of speed. But Jim had speed — nothing like the speed of lightning, but more like the speed of something round and smooth, such as cannon balls. Jim was, without question, a man of considerable courage, but in the case of my Rescue From the Lion, it was, I am told, his momentum rather than his bravery for which I must forever be grateful.

It happened like this — as Bishon Singh told it:

"I am resting against the walls of the place where hay is kept. First the large lion and then you, Beryl, pass me going toward the open field. A thought comes to me that a lion and a young girl are strange company, so I follow. I follow to the place where the hill that goes up becomes the hill that goes down. And where it goes down deepest, I see that you are running without much thought in your head. I see that the lion is running behind you with many thoughts in his head. Then I scream for everybody to come very fast.

"Everybody comes very fast. But the large lion is faster than anybody. He jumps on your back. I see you scream, but I hear no scream. I only hear the lion, and I begin to run with everybody, and this includes Mr. Elkington. He is saying a great many words I do not know. And he is carrying a long whip, which he holds in his hand and is meant for beating the large lion.

"Mr. Elkington goes past me, and he is waving the long whip so that it whistles over all of our heads like a very sharp wind. But when he gets close to the lion, it comes to my mind that that lion is not in the mood to be whipped.

"The lion is standing with the front of himself on your back, Beryl, and you are bleeding in three or five places, and he is roaring. The lion was looking as if he did not wish to be disturbed and he was saying so in a very large voice.

"I believe that Mr. Elkington understood this voice when he was still more than several feet from the lion. I believe he thought that it would be the best thing *not* to beat the lion just then. But Mr. Elkington was running very fast. He could not stop himself from rushing much closer to the lion than in his heart he wished to be.

"And, it was this circumstance, as I am telling it," said Mr. Singh, "which, in my opinion, made it possible for you to be alive, Beryl."

"Mr. Elkington rushed at the lion then, Bishon Singh?"

"The lion, on the contrary, rushed at Mr. Elkington," said Bishon Singh. "The lion deserted you for him. The lion was of the opinion that his master did not deserve any part of the fresh meat that he, the lion, had gotten all by himself."

"Fresh meat . . ." I repeated dreamily, and crossed my fingers. "So, then, what happened?"

Bishon Singh lifted his shoulders and let them drop again. "What could happen,

Beryl? The lion rushed for Mr. Elkington, who rushed from the lion. And in so rushing, he did not keep in his hand the long whip, but allowed it to fall upon the ground. So Mr. Elkington was free to climb a tree, which he did."

"And you picked me up, Bishon Singh?" He made a little dip with his turban. "I was happy with the duty of carrying you back to this very bed, Beryl. I told your father that you had been moderately eaten by the large lion. Your father returned very fast, and Mr. Elkington some time later returned very fast, but the large lion has not returned at all."

The large lion had not returned at all. That night he killed a horse, the next night he killed a yearling bullock, and after that a cow fresh for milking.

In the end he was caught and finally caged. He remained for years in his cage. But, had he managed to live in freedom as a tame lion, he might never been caged at all.

Paddy lived. People stared at him, and he stared back, and this went on until he was an old, old lion. Jim Elkington died. Mrs. Elkington really loved Paddy, but she was forced by circumstances beyond her control or Paddy's, to have him shot by Mr. Long, the manager of a nearby estate.

This was sad for Mr. Long, for no one loved animals more or understood them better. But Mr. Long could shoot cleanly, so Paddy died quickly.

But the result was the same to Paddy. He had lived and died in ways not of his choosing. He was a good lion. He had done what he could about being a tame lion. Is it fair that he was judged by a single error — trying to eat me?

I still have the scars of his teeth and claws, but they are very small now and almost forgotten, and I cannot begrudge him his moment. ◆

READING CHECK

Answer the following questions about "He Was a Good Lion." You may look back at the story if you want to.

1. How was the Elkington lion different from most lions? Why did Beryl's father say that this lion could not be trusted?

2. How did Beryl meet the lion? What did she do when she saw him?

3. Where did Bishon Singh see Beryl go? Why did he decide to follow her?

4. How did Mr. Elkington plan to rescue Beryl?

5. According to Bishon Singh, why did Paddy let go of Beryl?

6. After Paddy let Beryl go, what did Mr. Elkinton do? What did Bishon Singh do after that?

7. What happened to Paddy after Beryl's rescue? How did his life end?

WHAT DO YOU THINK?

1. Why did Beryl decide to walk slowly and sing brave sounding songs when she met Paddy? What would you have done if you were the one who came face to face with a lion?

2. Beryl did not hate Paddy for attacking her. Why do you think that she believed that "he was a good lion"?

3. Do you think it was right that Paddy was kept in a cage? Explain why or why not. If the decision had been up to you what would you have done with the lion?

VOCABULARY CHECK

Read the following sentences and choose the correct meaning of each word in **bold print.** Then write each word and its meaning on your paper.

1. Beryl went for a walk with no particular **destination** in mind.
   (specific place to travel to, specific map to follow)

2. Beryl did not see any sign of **menace** in Paddy's eyes.
   (threat of danger, glints of sun)

3. Because of an unlucky **circumstance** Beryl was hurt.
   (event, dinner)

4. Paddy would **begrudge** anyone's efforts to take away his fresh meat.
   (be afraid of, be angry with)

5. The girl was **sprawled** on the ground under the lion's paws.
   (crushed, stretched out)

6. When Beryl lived in Africa she learned **Swahili.**
   (an African language, an African hunting song)

7. Paddy was **contemptuous** of Mr. Elkington, after the man climbed the tree.
   (concerned about, had no respect for)

STRATEGY CHECK

The paragraph below is based on "He Was a Good Lion." Choose a word that makes sense to fill in each blank. Use the rest of the paragraph and what you remember about the story to help you. Then write the whole paragraph on your paper.

   Beryl and her father often went to visit the Elkingtons at their ___. As they rode along, Beryl's father told her that a ___ lion was an unnatural lion. One day Beryl came across Paddy the ___. She decided to ___ slowly and sing a song, but he attacked anyway. If Bishon Singh had not decided to follow ___ , she might not have lived to write her story.

"BURIED TREASURE"

Speed Armstrong makes fun of Brian and Pat and their plan to use their dog Clarence to help them search for buried treasure. In this story, Pat tells about their problems with Speed and a tight spot he gets into. Read this story to find out why Speed comes to change his mind about how useful Clarence can be in a search for buried treasure.

WORDS TO KNOW

The words in **bold print** are from "Buried Treasure." Study each word and its meaning carefully.

Clarence was **stalking** the crab along the beach.
  stalking — following as a hunter follows prey

Pat rested near the **dune** on the beach.
  dune — hill of loose sand found on a beach

Brian became **indignant** when Speed made fun of Clarence.
  indignant — angered by something unfair

No one had seen Clarence for hours, and it seemed as if the dog had **vanished.**
  vanished — disappeared

Because of bad storms, the sand hills on the beach **shifted** in the wind.
  shifted — moved, changed direction

They heard a **muffled** voice calling for help.
  muffled — softened because of being covered or buried

When Brian got the reward his face turned **fiery** red.
  fiery — like fire, the color of fire.

BURIED TREASURE

by PATRICIA LAUBER

Clarence was tracking. Nose to the sand, he was stalking a small sand crab. When the crab stopped, Clarence stopped and pointed. When the crab scuttled forward, Clarence followed. He was concentrating so hard that he didn't even notice when someone came over the dune and sat down beside Brian and me.

The new arrival was a boy we'd seen around. He was younger than we were, and tough-looking. The boy said, "I'm Speed Armstrong. Who are you?"

I told him my name was Patricia and then I told him my brother's name, Brian. Then he looked at Clarence. "Is that your dog?"

"Yes," I said, "that's Clarence."

Speed hooted with laughter. "Clarence! What a name for a dog! Who ever heard of a dog called Clarence?"

"It's a very good name for a dog," Brian said angrily. "Do you have a dog?"

"I've got something better," Speed said. "I'm building a rocket. As a matter of fact, you're sitting on my rocket site."

Brian and I looked around.

"I mean," Speed said, "when I finish building my rocket, I'm going to launch it from here."

"That's dangerous," Brian said. "You might blow yourself up."

"Of course it's dangerous," Speed boasted. "But I'm not afraid. I bet you're a sissy — and so's your dog. Any dog with a name like Clarence is bound to be."

Brian scrambled to his feet and looked angry.

Speed paid no attention to Brian. "You should see Boy. He belongs to our neighbor, and he's a *real* dog. He's huge, and he has

great big bulging muscles that ripple when he walks."

"I imagine he's stupid," Brian said. "All muscle and no brain." As he spoke, he looked meaningfully at Speed's muscles.

"No, he isn't," Speed said. "He's very highly trained. All you have to do is say the word and he attacks."

"What word?" I asked.

Speed didn't answer.

"Yah!" Brian said. "You don't even know."

"Of course not," Speed answered. "Boy was right there while Mr. Gunn was telling me. If he'd said the word, Boy might have torn my arm off. Sometimes Mr. Gunn lets me take Boy out. He and I are the only two people who can handle Boy."

"Oh, great!" I said. "Who wants a dog like that?"

"*I* do," Speed said. "When the government buys my rocket plans from me, I'm going to buy a big dog just like Boy."

Brian and I looked at each other. Then

valuable dog in him," Brian said. "That's why he's such a good hunter and tracker. See how he points?"

"Points?" Speed said. "Dogs don't point with their hind paws. They point with their front paws."

"Most dogs do," Brian said, "because they only know how to point with their front paws. Clarence can point with any paw."

Just then the crab went down its hole. Clarence began to dig furiously. Pretty soon all we could see of him was his hind legs.

Brian said, "Clarence is a very good digger."

I said, "Clarence is good at everything."

Not to be outdone, Brian said, "In fact, Clarence is so good at hunting and tracking and digging that I'm going to use him to hunt buried treasure."

Speed howled with laughter and fell over backward. "Ah-ha-ha! That's the funniest thing I've ever heard — using a dog to hunt buried treasure."

"I don't see what's so funny about it," Brian said. "It's a good idea."

"That's all you know!" Speed snorted. "It's so silly that I'd bet my rocket Clarence couldn't find any buried treasure if he stayed here for a hundred years."

"All right!" Brian said. "We'll show you."

Just then Clarence gave up digging for the sand crab and trotted toward us.

For a moment, I almost wished Clarence was the kind of dog who bit strangers. But he loves meeting people, so he jumped all

Brian said, "I don't believe you have a rocket. I think you're making it up."

Speed laughed. "Well, I'm not going to prove it by showing you my rocket. All important rocket work is top secret. Nobody's seen my rocket and nobody even knows where I work on it, except Boy. Sometimes I take him along to stand guard." Speed looked back at Clarence. "What's he doing now?"

"He's tracking," I said.

"Clarence has quite a few kinds of very

over Speed and licked his face.

Speed held Clarence off and studied him. "He's pretty small," Speed said thoughtfully.

"But very intelligent," I said.

"His tail curls just right," Speed went on.

"Right for what?" Brian asked.

"Right for fitting into my rocket. You've got to have a small dog with a curly tail."

I gasped. Even Brian was speechless.

Speed got up. "Be seeing you," he said, and strolled off.

Brian found his voice. "Not if we see you first," he said, but Speed was gone.

That evening we went to see Uncle Matt and told him the whole story. Uncle Matt didn't think we had much to worry about. "Speed's a regular teller of tall tales," Uncle Matt explained. "Just last year he told everybody he was raising a tiger. Turned out to be a plain, ordinary cat that was tiger-striped. Uncle Matt said, "Boy is most likely a Pekingese, and the rocket's a burned-out firecracker."

We felt much better after hearing that. So Brian brought up the matter of hunting buried treasure. He told Uncle Matt about the bet. "I was just boasting back when I said it," Brian confessed. "But it does seem like a pretty good idea."

Uncle Matt didn't know of any buried treasure around these parts, but he suggested we talk to Mr. Tolliver. "He's interested in the history of the Cape," Uncle Matt explained. "Maybe he's turned up something in all those old books and

maps he has."

The next morning we went to see the Tollivers. Mr. Tolliver agreed with Uncle Matt that our chances of finding buried treasure were pretty slim. And he laughed at the idea of Speed sending Clarence up in a rocket. "Why," he said, "it would take half a dozen top scientists to do that."

Mrs. Tolliver, though, was indignant. "The very idea," she said. "Imagine even joking about sending Clarence up in a rocket!" Then she went away and brought out a big bone with huge chunks of meat on it. "I was going to make soup from this," she said, "but I can always get another one. May Clarence have it?"

It was the most beautiful bone Clarence had ever had. He took it into the shade and began to work on it. He was still chewing by the time Brian and I were ready to leave. The Tollivers said Clarence was welcome to stay and finish his bone, but Clarence decided he'd rather come with us and bring his bone.

It wasn't easy going, for the bone was big and Clarence's mouth is small. Clarence kept having to put the bone down and take a fresh grip on it. Brian and I both offered to carry the bone. But Clarence thought so highly of it that he wouldn't trust it even to us.

We were heading home along the beach when someone called us. There was Speed coming down the dunes. Beside him, on the end of a chain, stalked a huge dog.

Brian and I stood and stared. Clarence, who was standing near us, laid down his bone on the sand. Then he went forward, tail wagging, to sniff at Boy.

Boy snarled.

Speed tightened his grip on the chain. "You better keep your dog away," he warned.

Brian scooped up Clarence.

"Isn't Boy something?" Speed asked. "Did you ever see such a dog?"

At that moment, Boy lunged. Speed managed to hang onto the chain, but it didn't matter. Boy had seized Clarence's bone.

Clarence squirmed and whimpered in Brian's arms. "You give that back!" Brian said. "That's Clarence's bone."

"Tough!" Speed said.

"That's stealing," I said. "Mrs. Tolliver gave that bone to Clarence."

"I can't give it back," Speed said. "You don't think Boy's going to give it up, do you?"

"I thought you could handle Boy," Brian said.

"I can!" Speed insisted. "But there's no need to. My rocket's almost ready now. And there isn't room for Clarence *and* the bone." Speed strolled off with Boy and the bone.

We had to carry Clarence home to keep him from going after Boy. Clarence was very unhappy. We were unhappy, too. Speed hadn't been exaggerating. Boy was just as big and fierce as he had said. And this meant that he really might be building a rocket.

When Aunt Jo heard what had happened, she gave Clarence a plate of chicken meat at lunch and promised him a new bone. Clarence soon cheered up.

Brian and I were still worried, though. And you can imagine what we felt like when Clarence disappeared. One minute he was poking around in some bushes. The next minute he was gone. We called and whistled, but he didn't come. We telephoned all the friends he might be visiting. But Clarence had vanished.

Brian was all for calling the police and having Speed arrested. I thought we'd better ask Uncle Matt first.

Uncle Matt listened to our story. Then he said, "Well, even if Speed wasn't exaggerating about Boy, that still doesn't prove he's planning to send Clarence up in a rocket."

"Then where is Clarence?" I asked. "He never goes wandering off for the whole afternoon this way."

Uncle Matt thought. "Tell you what," he said. "Suppose we start by calling Speed's family." He went to the phone. "Mrs. Armstrong?" we heard him say. "This is Matthew Gregory. Is Speed home? No, I wanted to ask him . . . What?" A look of concern came over Uncle Matt's face. "He did? No, Pat and Brian saw them this morning. Just a minute."

Uncle Matt turned to us. "Speed has disappeared. Boy came home alone before noon. But nobody's seen Speed since this morning. Where was he when you saw him?"

We described the place.

Uncle Matt repeated what we'd said. "All right, we'll meet him there." He hung up the phone. "Come on," he said to us. "Mrs. Armstrong called the police. We're going to meet Sergeant Wood on the beach where you saw Speed this morning."

The sergeant was waiting for us beside a jeep that he had driven along the wet sand. We told him the whole story.

The sergeant frowned thoughtfully and stared down the beach. "Did you think they were going to the secret rocket place this morning?"

"I thought so," I said, "but Speed didn't really say."

Uncle Matt had a suggestion. "What about getting this dog Boy to lead you to the place?"

"I tried that," the sergeant said, "but he just snarled at me and went back to sleep. He didn't seem to get the idea at all."

"Clarence could track Speed," Brian said. "If we could find Clarence, he'd find Speed. Can't we look for Clarence first?"

The sergeant grinned. "We'll look for them both at the same time. Hop into the jeep and we'll take a drive along the beach."

As Uncle Matt, Brian, and I watched for signs of Speed and Clarence, the sergeant told us that Speed's family didn't know anything about his rocket. What had started them worrying was Speed's absence at lunch. Speed might vanish for hours at a time, but he never missed a meal.

Sergeant Wood had hardly finished telling us all this, when Brian shouted, "Look, Pat! There's Clarence! I see him!"

Far down the beach, a small dog was standing on the sand looking in our direction. The sergeant stepped on the gas. When he stopped, Brian and I piled out of the jeep. It was Clarence! He was perfectly fine, except that he seemed a little tired. He also had something on his mind. As soon as he'd greeted all of us, he trotted off a few steps and then looked back at Brian and me to see if we were coming.

We followed him up the beach. The dunes here were very high. At their foot was a great pile of sand with some planks and beams sticking out of it. Clarence had spent the afternoon digging here. There were holes in the pile of sand, holes in the beach around it.

Uncle Matt and Sergeant Wood looked at all this. Then they looked at each other.

The sergeant said, "Wasn't there a hut here once?"

Uncle Matt nodded. "Belonged to some fisherman. Then, in that bad storm two or three winters ago, the dunes shifted. The hut was swallowed up in sand."

The sergeant said thoughtfully, "Do you suppose —"

"Might be," Uncle Matt said. "I don't think the whole hut collapsed."

Looking very concerned, the sergeant hurried toward the remains of the hut. "Ahoy!" he yelled.

A faint voice called, "Help!"

"Speed!" the sergeant yelled. "You in there?"

"Yes," the muffled voice replied.

Sergeant Wood ran back to the jeep for shovels. Then, working with great care, he and Uncle Matt began to dig.

Clarence was delighted. He began to dig, too.

In a matter of minutes, Sergeant Wood, Uncle Matt, and Clarence had made a big hole. Speed crawled out through it. Clarence went on digging as Sergeant Wood pulled Speed to his feet.

"You all right?" he demanded.

"I guess so." Speed was blinking and squinting in the light.

"Of all the fool things to do!" Uncle Matt said. "What did you do — blow the place up with your rocket?"

"No," Speed said in a small voice. "I couldn't. I mean, it wasn't a real rocket. It was just a model."

"Then what happened?" the sergeant demanded.

Speed explained that a few months ago he had discovered the hut buried in sand and tunneled into it. Part of the hut had collapsed, but part was still standing. Speed had shored up the opening, and used the hut as a secret place to keep his rocket. Everything had been fine until this morning.

"Boy found a bone," Speed said.

"He did not," Brian said. "He stole it from Clarence."

Speed blinked in Brian's direction. "Oh,"

he said, "are you here? I still can't see in the light."

"All right," the sergeant prompted. "Boy had a bone."

"Well," Speed went on, "I didn't see what happened, but I guess he decided to bury it. I heard him digging near me. The next thing I knew, the tunnel was collapsing and Boy was gone."

"Weren't you scared?" Brian asked.

"A little," Speed admitted. "But I knew Boy would save me. First he went away. When he couldn't get help, he came back. He's been trying to dig me out for two or three hours."

"Boy!" Sergeant Wood snorted. "It's Clarence who's been trying to dig you out. Boy buried you along with his bone and then went home and forgot about both of you. If it hadn't been for Clarence, you might have been here for a week before we found you." He took Speed by the arm. "Come on. Your mother's sick with worry."

Uncle Matt drove off with them. Brian and I said we'd walk home with Clarence. This time Clarence let me carry the bone, which he'd found shortly after Uncle Matt and Sergeant Wood had rescued Speed.

The next day Mrs. Armstrong came to call on us, bringing Speed. She wanted to meet Clarence and Brian and me and thank us for rescuing Speed. Then she made Speed apologize for having said he was going to send Clarence up in a rocket.

Red-faced, Speed said he was sorry. "I was only teasing," he explained, squatting and patting Clarence. "I wouldn't really do a thing like that." Clarence took a nip at Speed's nose. "Clarence and I are friends," Speed said. "I wouldn't hurt him."

Mrs. Armstrong had brought Clarence a new collar. Attached to it was a little medal that read: CLARENCE — *for bravery*. She sent Speed to the car for a huge box, which he gave to Brian. It was a model rocket kit.

Brian didn't know what to say.

Mrs. Armstrong said, "Speed told me he'd bet that Clarence couldn't find any buried treasure."

"But —" Brian began.

"Oh, I know," Mrs. Armstrong said. "You think of buried treasure as a chest of jewels. But Speed is my treasure."

Speed's face turned fiery red. "Aw, Ma," he said. "Cut it out."

For the first time, I began to feel sorry for Speed. I mean, our mother may think Brian and I are treasures, but she'd never say so in public.

After the Armstrongs had left, Brian took me aside for a talk. Finally, we decided to put the problem to Aunt Jo and Uncle Matt.

"I don't think I should keep the rocket kit," Brian said.

"Why not?" asked Aunt Jo.

"Because Clarence had tracked Boy and was just trying to find his bone," I explained.

"And neither the bone nor Speed is really treasure," Brian added.

Aunt Jo and Uncle Matt said nothing.

"Mother likes us to be honest," I said.

Aunt Jo smiled at us. "I think you could keep them," she said. "You must remember that treasure can mean different things to different people. Mrs. Armstrong would much rather have Speed than a chest of jewels. And Clarence would rather have his bone."

"Besides," Uncle Matt said, "you don't know that Clarence was just digging for his bone. He may have known that Speed was trapped. After all, he's a very intelligent dog."

That was certainly true. In fact, the more we thought about it, the more we began to believe that Clarence had been trying to rescue Speed. Anyway, that was the story printed in the town newspaper the following week. It had a big headline that said: DOG SAVES LOCAL BOY. Then there was a long story about how Speed had been buried. It told how Clarence had tried to dig Speed out. Sergeant Wood told how Clarence had led the search party to the buried hut. Then Speed was quoted as saying what a fine, brave, intelligent dog Clarence was. At the very end, Speed said, "I'm going to get me a dog just like Clarence."

"Humph!" Brian said when he read that. "There aren't any dogs just like Clarence." ◆

READING CHECK

Answer the following questions about "Buried Treasure." You may look back at the story if you want to.

1. Where did Pat and Brian first meet Speed? What was Clarence doing at the time?

2. What did Speed tell Pat and Brian that he had that was better than having a dog? How would you describe Speed's behavior?

3. What unusual thing did Brian want Speed to think Clarence could do? What caused Brian to make up this story?

4. What was Uncle Matt's opinion of Speed? What example did Uncle Matt give Brian and Pat to back up that opinion? How did this information make Brian and Pat feel?

5. What action did Brian want to take when Clarence disappeared? Who called the police, and why?

6. What accident occurred when Boy tried to bury the bone he had stolen from Clarence?

7. Who first found Speed? How was Speed rescued?

WHAT DO YOU THINK?

1. At first, Brian didn't feel quite right about accepting the model rocket from Speed's mother. Do you think he should have taken it? What do you think you'd do if you were given a reward and weren't sure why?

2. What do you think Clarence was really trying to dig up, his long lost bone or Speed? Give reasons to explain your answer.

3. What do you think might have caused Speed to make up the story about the rocket and to make fun of Clarence? How would you feel about someone who went around making up wild stories and insulting people, or making fun of their pets? Explain what you would do if you had to spend a lot of time around a person like Speed.

VOCABULARY CHECK

Read the following sentences and choose the correct meaning of each word in **bold print.** Then write each word and its meaning on your paper.

1. Pat was **indignant** when Speed made fun of her brother's ideas.
   (angered, surprised)

2. Crabs scuttled around the **dune.**
   (hill of sand, pool of water)

3. Clarence moved as if he was **stalking** food.
   (digging, hunting)

4. The strong wind was the reason the sand **shifted.**
   (blew in people's faces, changed direction)

5. A day at the beach can lead to a **fiery** sunburn.
   (fairly bad, like the color of fire)

6. The **muffled** sound of a voice could be heard from beneath the hill.
   (softened, screaming)

7. Speed **vanished,** and no one could find him.
   (disappeared, disappointed)

STRATEGY CHECK

The paragraph below is based on the story "Buried Treasure." Choose a word that makes sense to fill in each blank. Use the rest of the paragraph and what you remember about the story to help you. Then write the whole paragraph on your paper.

Speed talked a lot about the ＿＿ he was building. When he said Clarence's curly ＿＿ would fit in the rocket, Brian and Pat were worried about their dog's safety. But it was Speed who met with danger, and Clarence rescued him from the remains of a ＿＿ covered with sand. Speed confessed that the rocket was only a ＿＿, not a real rocket. For saving her son, Mrs. Armstrong gave Clarence a new ＿＿ with a medal for bravery attached to it.

◆ INTRODUCING ◆
"THE THINKING MACHINE, PART 1"

"The Thinking Machine" is not the name of a new kind of computer — it is the nickname of a man who became famous for thinking his way out of many difficult situations. The Thinking Machine believes that the mind is the master of all things. In this story he decides to prove he can think his way out of anything — even a locked prison cell.

WORDS TO KNOW

The words in **bold print** are from "The Thinking Machine, Part 1." Study each word and its meaning carefully.

The wall was so high and smooth no one could **scale** it.
    scale — climb

They **deciphered** some words that had been written on a cloth.
    deciphered — were able to read or understand

A **dreadful** scream sounded through the prison.
    dreadful — terrible

They heard the **piercing** cry again.
    piercing — sharp, cutting

THE THINKING MACHINE
PART 1

by JACQUES FUTRELLE

The world knew of Professor Van Dusen as The Thinking Machine. The name was given to him in a newspaper article about a remarkable chess game the professor had played. He showed that someone who had never played chess before could use his brain to defeat a great chess champion.

The Thinking Machine spent week after week in his small laboratory. Sometimes visitors dropped in to discuss a scientific problem. One evening, two men, Dr. Charles Ransome and Alfred Fielding, called on the professor.

The three men talked about a favorite subject — the mind. "The mind is the master of all things," declared The Thinking Machine.

Dr. Ransome laughed. "There are some problems that no amount of thinking can solve," he said.

"What, for example?" demanded the Professor.

Dr. Ransome was thoughtful for a moment. "Well, say prison walls," he replied. "No man can *think* himself out of a cell. If he could, there would be no prisoners."

"A man can use his brain so that he can leave a cell," snapped The Thinking Machine.

Dr. Ransome was amused. "Suppose you were locked in a cell, could you escape?"

"Certainly," declared The Thinking Machine. "Lock me in any cell in any prison, and I'll escape in a week." Dr. Ransome and Mr. Fielding were silent for a moment.

"Would you be willing to try it immediately?" asked Fielding.

"Yes," said The Thinking Machine.

"Say, the maximum security cell in Chisholm Prison?"

"Yes," said the Thinking Machine.

"And what will you wear?"

"As little as possible," said The Thinking Machine. "A shirt, trousers, shoes, and socks."

"You will permit yourself to be searched, of course?"

"I am to be treated exactly as all prisoners are treated," said The Thinking Machine.

All the details for the test were arranged by telephone. The prison officials agreed to the experiment, but they were bewildered. Professor Van Dusen would be the most distinguished prisoner they had ever had.

The Thinking Machine put on the clothes he would wear during his imprisonment. Then he called his housekeeper.

"Martha," he said, "it is now almost 9:30. One week from tonight at 9:30, these gentlemen and one or two others will take supper with me here."

The three men drove to Chisholm Prison, where the warden was awaiting them. He understood that Professor Van Dusen was to be his prisoner for one week, that he had committed no crime, but that he was to be treated like all other prisoners.

"Search him," instructed Dr. Ransome.

The Thinking Machine was searched. Nothing was found on him. The pockets of his trousers were empty. His white shirt with the stiff front had no pocket. The shoes and socks were removed, examined, and then replaced.

Dr. Ransome asked the warden: "Will it be impossible for him to communicate with anyone outside?"

"Absolutely impossible," replied the warden. "He will not be allowed writing materials of any sort."

"And your guards? Would they deliver a message from him?"

"Not one word," said the warden. "They will report anything he might say, or turn over to me anything he might give them."

"That seems satisfactory," said Fielding.

The Thinking Machine stood listening until all talk was ended. Then he said, "I would like to make three small requests. I would like to have some tooth powder. And I would like to have one five-dollar and two ten-dollar bills."

Dr. Ransome, Fielding, and the warden exchanged glances. They were not surprised at the request for tooth powder, but the request for money startled them.

"Is there any man whom the professor would meet that he could bribe with 25 dollars?" Dr. Ransome asked the warden.

"Not for 2,500 dollars," was the reply.

"Well, then, let him have the money," said Fielding.

"And what is the third request?" asked Dr. Ransome.

"I would like to have my shoes polished." The others looked astonished, but they

agreed to the request at once. The Thinking Machine was led to his cell.

"Here is Cell 13," said the warden, stopping three doors down the steel corridor from his office. "No one can leave it without my permission, and no one can communicate with anyone outside."

The heavy steel door was thrown open. There was a great scurrying of tiny feet, and The Thinking Machine passed into the gloom of the cell. Then the door was closed and double-locked by the warden.

"What is that noise in there?" asked Dr. Ransome through the bars.

"Rats — dozens of them," replied The Thinking Machine.

The three men were turning away when The Thinking Machine called: "Exactly what time is it now, warden?"

"11:17" replied the warden.

"Thank you. I will join you gentlemen in your office at 8:30 one week from tonight," said The Thinking Machine.

Chisholm Prison was a large building, four stories high. It was surrounded by a stone wall 18 feet high and so smooth that no one could possibly scale it.

There were four armed guards in the prison yard, one patrolling each side of the prison building. At night, the yard was almost as brightly lit as by day. On each of the four sides, a great arc light rose above the prison wall and gave the guards a clear view. The wires to the arc lights ran up the side of the prison building. From the top story, these wires led out to the poles

supporting the lights.

On the morning after he had been locked in the cell, all these things were noticed by The Thinking Machine. He could see out of his barred window by standing on his bed. He gathered, too, that a river lay somewhere beyond the wall because he could hear the sound of a motorboat, and high up in the air, he saw a river bird.

From the same direction came the shouts of children at play and sometimes, the crack of a batted ball. He knew, then, that between the prison wall and the river was an open space, a playground.

Chisholm Prison was regarded as absolutely safe. No one had ever escaped from it. The Thinking Machine could understand why. The walls of the cell were perfectly solid, and the bars were made of steel. Even with the bars removed, the window would be a difficult way out because it was small.

Yet, The Thinking Machine was not discouraged. Instead, he squinted at the great arc light and traced with his eyes the wire that led to the building. The electric wire, he reasoned, must come down the side of the building fairly close to his cell. *That might be worth noting.*

The Thinking Machine examined his cell. There was nothing in the cell except his iron bed. There was not even a chair, or a small table. There was not even a bowl for eating. When the guard came with a meal, he took away the wooden bowl and spoon the prisoner had used.

One by one, these things sank into the brain of The Thinking Machine. But his thinking was disturbed by a rat, which ran across his foot, then ran away into a dark corner of the cell. The Thinking Machine stared into that corner. After a while, he was able to make out many little beady eyes staring at him.

Seated on his bed, he noticed for the first time the bottom of his cell door. There was an opening of two inches between the steel bar and the floor. Looking steadily at this opening, The Thinking Machine backed suddenly into the corner where he had seen the beady eyes. There was a great scampering of tiny feet, several frightened squeaks, and then silence.

None of the rats had gone out the door, yet there were none in the cell. Therefore, there must be another way out of the cell.

The Thinking Machine got down on his hands and knees. He searched for this spot in the darkness, feeling with his long, slender fingers.

At last, his search was rewarded. He came upon a small opening in the floor. It was perfectly round and somewhat larger than a silver dollar. This was the way the rats had gone. He put his fingers into the opening; it seemed to be an unused drainpipe and was dry and dusty.

Noon came, and the guard appeared with the prison meal. The Thinking Machine asked a few questions while the guard watched him eat.

"Any improvements made here in the

last few years?"

"Nothing special," replied the guard. "A new wall was built four years ago."

"Anything done to the prison building?"

"I believe about seven years ago, a new system of plumbing was put in."

"Ah!" said the prisoner. "How far is the river over there?"

"About 300 feet," said the guard. "The kids have a playground between the wall and the river."

The Thinking Machine had no more questions, but he asked if the guard could leave a little water in a bowl for him. The jailer went to ask the warden and soon returned with a small bowl of water.

"The warden says you may keep this bowl," he told the prisoner, "but you must show it to me when I ask for it. If it is broken, you won't get another one."

Two hours later, the guard passed the door of Cell 13, heard a noise inside, and stopped. The Thinking Machine was down on his hands and knees in a corner of the cell.

"Ah, I've got you," he heard the prisoner say.

"Got what?" the guard asked sharply.

"One of these rats," was the answer. The prisoner brought the rat to the light and looked at it closely. "It's a field rat," he said.

Still later that day, a guard outside the prison looked up at the window of Cell 13 and saw the prisoner looking out. He saw a hand raised to the barred window. Then something white fluttered to the ground. It was a little roll of white cloth, and tied around it was a five-dollar bill. The guard looked up at the window again, but the face had disappeared.

With a smile, the guard took the roll of cloth and the five-dollar bill to the warden's office. There, they deciphered some words on the outside of the roll of cloth. Written with an odd sort of ink, and often blurred, was this message: *Finder of this, please deliver to Dr. Charles Ransome.*

"Ah," said the warden, with a chuckle. "Plan of escape number one has gone wrong." Then he asked, "But why did he address it to Dr. Ransome?"

"And where did he get the pen and ink to write with?" asked the guard.

The warden studied the writing carefully. "Well, let's see what he was going to say to Dr. Ransome," he said at last. Still puzzled, he unrolled the inner piece of cloth. He read the message and showed it to the guard. This is what it said:

Epa cseot d'net niiy awe htto n'si sih."T."

The warden wondered what sort of code the Professor had used, and why he should try to communicate with Dr. Ransome. He also wondered where the prisoner had found a pen and ink to write with. The warden examined the piece of cloth again. The edges were ragged, and he could see that it was the torn part of a white shirt.

The warden then went to Cell 13 and found The Thinking Machine on his hands and knees on the floor. He was busy catching rats. The prisoner heard the warden's step and turned to him quickly.

"It's disgraceful, these rats," he snapped. "There are so many of them."

"Other men have been able to stand them," said the warden. "Here is another shirt for you — let me have the one you have on."

"Why?" asked the prisoner.

"You have tried to contact Dr. Ransome," said the warden severely. "You are a prisoner, and it is my duty to put a stop to that."

The prisoner got up from the floor and changed into the striped prison shirt the warden had brought. The warden took the white shirt eagerly. He compared the cloth on which the code was written with certain torn places in the shirt.

"What did you write this code with?" demanded the warden.

"I think it's part of your job to find out!"

The warden started to say something, but restrained himself. He made a careful search of the cell and the prisoner. He found absolutely nothing, not even a match or toothpick which might have been used as a pen. He also found nothing that could have been used for the ink.

On the third day of his imprisonment, The Thinking Machine tried to bribe his way out. He began the conversation when the guard brought his dinner.

"The drainpipes of the prison lead to the river, don't they?" he asked.

"Yes," replied the guard.

"I suppose they are very small?" asked the prisoner.

"Too small to crawl through, if that's what you're thinking about," the guard said with a grin.

"Well, I came here believing that I could make my escape," said the prisoner. "Would you consider a financial reward for helping me to escape?"

The guard, who was an honest man, looked at the slender, weak figure of the prisoner, and was almost sorry.

"Prisons like this were not built for the likes of you to get out of," he said, shaking his head.

"But would you consider a plan to help me get out?" urged The Thinking Machine. "I am not a criminal, you know."

"No," said the guard shortly.

"I'll give you 1,000 dollars."

"No," said the guard again. "Even if you gave me 10,000 dollars, I couldn't get you out. You'd have to pass through seven doors, and I only have the keys to two."

The guard went directly to the warden and told him of the professor's offer.

"Plan number two fails," said the warden. "First a code, then bribery."

At 6:00, the guard was on his way to Cell 13 with food for The Thinking Machine. He paused and listened intently, for he heard the scrape, scrape of steel against steel. It stopped at the sound of his footsteps.

After a moment, he heard it again — the steady scrape, scrape. The guard tiptoed to the door and peered between the bars. The Thinking Machine was standing on the iron

bed working at the bars of the little window, scraping back and forth.

Cautiously, the guard left to call the warden. The steady scrape could still be heard when the two men returned to Cell 13.

"Well?" demanded the warden. There was a satisfied smile on his face.

The Thinking Machine leaped suddenly from his perch on the bed and made frantic efforts to hide something. The warden went in with his hand out.

"Give it up," he said.

"No!" said the prisoner sharply.

"Come, give it up," urged the warden.

"No," repeated the prisoner.

"What was it, a file?" asked the warden.

The Thinking Machine was silent and stood squinting at the warden with disappointment on his face. The warden was almost sympathetic.

"Plan number three fails, eh?" he asked good-naturedly.

The prisoner did not answer.

"Search him," instructed the warden.

The guard searched the prisoner carefully. At last he found two pieces of steel hidden in the waistband of the trousers, each about two inches long, with curved sides.

"Ah," said the warden as he received them from the guard. "From your shoe heels," and he smiled pleasantly. "You couldn't saw through those bars with these."

"I could have," said The Thinking Machine firmly.

The warden shook his head slowly as he gazed into the slightly flushed face of his prisoner.

"Ready to give it up?" he asked.

"I've hardly started yet," was the reply.

The warden climbed on the bed and examined the bars of the window which the prisoner had been sawing. He grasped the bars in his hands and tried to shake them. They couldn't be moved. Finally, he climbed down from the bed.

"Give it up, Professor," he advised.

The Thinking Machine shook his head, and the warden and guard left the cell.

At 4:00 the next morning, a strange thing happened. A dreadful scream sounded through the great prison — a shriek of pure terror. The warden rushed with three of his men into the long corridor leading to Cell 13.

As they ran down the corridor, they heard it again — an awful cry that died away in a sort of wail.

"It's that fool in Cell 13," grumbled the warden.

He stopped and stared as one of the guards flashed a light. "That fool in Cell 13" lay comfortably on his bed, sleeping with his mouth open. Suddenly, there came again the piercing cry, from somewhere above. Directly above Cell 13, two floors higher, was Cell 33. There the warden found a prisoner sobbing in a corner of his cell.

"Take me out, take me out," he screamed. "I did it, I did it."

"Did what?" asked the warden. He turned to a guard. "Who is this fellow? What's he accused of?"

"Joseph Ballard," the guard replied. "He's accused of throwing acid in a woman's face."

"I did it. I confess," screamed the prisoner. "Only take me away from that terrible sound."

"He's insane," said one of the guards.

"He must be," the warden said, "but he certainly heard something that frightened him." ◆

READING CHECK

Answer the following questions about "The Thinking Machine, Part 1." You may look back at the story if you want to.

1. How did The Thinking Machine get his nickname?

2. Why did The Thinking Machine suggest that he should be locked up in a prison cell? When did he expect to get out of prison?

3. What three things did The Thinking Machine ask for when he was brought to the prison?

4. On the first day in prison, how did The Thinking Machine know that there was a playground near the prison?

5. On the second day, what message did the guard find tied to a five dollar bill? When the warden examined the message, what strange things did he discover?

6. What happened when The Thinking Machine tried to bribe the guard? What happened when he tried to saw through the bars in the window?

7. Who was screaming early the next morning and why? What was The Thinking Machine doing at that time?

WHAT DO YOU THINK?

1. Do you think that The Thinking Machine expected the guard to take the bribe he offered? If not, what other possible reasons could he have had for offering it?
2. Does the warden believe that The Thinking Machine is clever enough to escape from the prison? Explain your answer.
3. What does The Thinking Machine mean when he says "The mind is master of all things"?

VOCABULARY CHECK

Read the following sentences and choose the correct meaning of each word in **bold print.** Then write each word and its meaning on your paper.

1. No one could **scale** the walls of the prison.
    (tunnel through, climb over)

2. At 4 o'clock in the morning, the warden heard a **piercing** scream.
    (sobbing, sharp)

3. It was **dreadful** that rats ran through the cell.
    (noisy, terrible)

4. They **deciphered** the message The Thinking Machine had sent.
    (were able to destroy, were able to read)

STRATEGY CHECK

The paragraph below is based on "The Thinking Machine, Part 1." Choose a word that makes sense to fill in each blank. Use the rest of the paragraph and what you remember about the story to help you. Then write the whole paragraph on your paper.

The Thinking Machine believed that his ___ could get him out of any difficult stituation. That's why he agreed to be locked up in a ___ cell as a test. He agreed that the ___ should treat him just like any other prisoner. The warden watched him carefully. When he heard a strange noise, he took away the tool The Thinking Machine was using to ___ through the bars on the window. The Thinking Machine also offered money to the ___ to open the doors, but this did not work.

"THE THINKING MACHINE, PART 2"

The Thinking Machine has only four more days to prove he can escape from his cell. Then the experiment is over. Will he make it? Read the rest of the story to find out.

WORDS TO KNOW

The words in **bold print** are from "The Thinking Machine, Part 2." Study each word and its meaning carefully.

The warden was almost in a **trance** when he saw The Thinking Machine and the reporter at the door.
   trance — a state almost like being in a deep sleep

The Thinking Machine **moistened** shoe polish with water to make ink.
   moistened — wet

When the reporter learned of the experiment, he **immediately** knew it would make a good story.
   immediately — instantly

Mr. Hatch gave the boy another ten dollars to get some **twine** and wire.
   twine — a strong string made of twisted thread

When he was sure the **current** was off, The Thinking Machine cut the wires to the lights.
   current — electricity flowing through a wire

THE THINKING MACHINE

PART 2

On his fourth day in prison, The Thinking Machine spent most of his time at the little window of his cell. The guard outside had seen other prisoners stand and stare the same way.

Once The Thinking Machine spoke to the guard.

"Who attends to those arc lights?" he asked.

"Man from the electric company."

"You have no electricians in the building?"

"No."

In the afternoon, the prisoner threw another piece of cloth down to the guard, who picked it up and took it to the warden. On it was written: *Only three days more.*

The warden was not surprised at what he read. He understood that the Professor meant only three days more of his imprisonment, and he regarded the note as a boast. But how was the note written?

Where had The Thinking Machine found this new piece of cloth?

The warden examined the cloth carefully. It was white material of fine texture. He examined the shirt which he had taken from the Professor. He carefully fitted the two original pieces of cloth to the torn places. The third piece didn't fit anywhere. Yet it was definitely the same material.

"And where — where does he get anything to write with?" the warden asked himself.

Then and there he made up his mind. He would search Cell 13 as a cell had never been searched before. He decided to enter the cell at 3:00 AM.

If the warden had planned to startle The Thinking Machine, he was disappointed. The scientist merely opened his eyes, reached for his glasses, and asked in a matter-of-fact tone, "Who is it?"

The warden's search was thorough. Not

one inch of the cell or the bed was overlooked. He found the round hole in the floor and put his thick fingers into it. After a moment of fumbling, he pulled something up and looked at it. It was a dead rat.

Next, the warden climbed on the bed and tried the steel bars in the tiny window. They were perfectly tight. Every bar of the door was also secure.

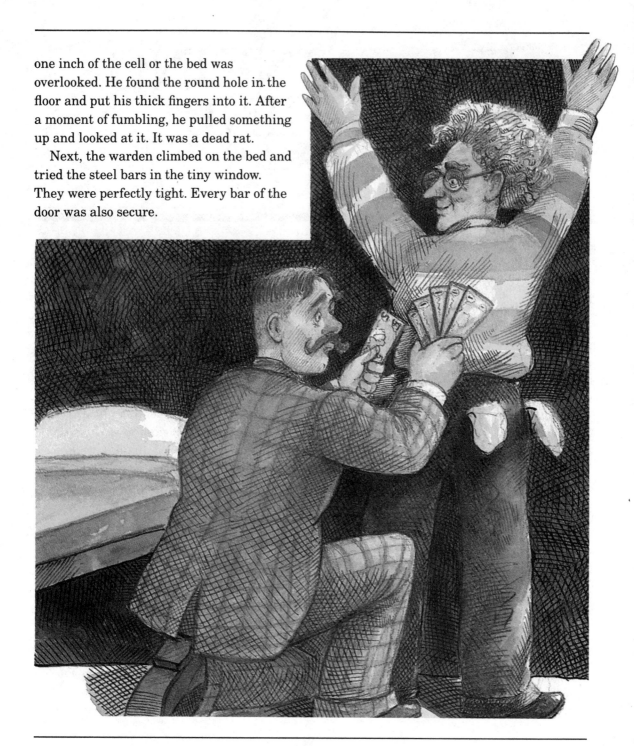

Then the warden searched the prisoner's clothing. From one pocket he drew out some paper money and examined it.

"A five-dollar bill and five one-dollar bills," he gasped. "But you had only two tens and a five, and the five is in my desk drawer. How do you do it?"

"That's my business," said The Thinking Machine.

"Did any of my men change this money for you — on your word of honor?"

The Thinking Machine paused just a fraction of a second.

"No," he said.

The warden glared at the scientist. He knew that this man was making a fool of him, yet he didn't know how. Neither man spoke. Then the warden turned and left the cell, slamming the door behind him.

When the fifth day of The Thinking Machine's imprisonment rolled around, the warden was wearing a hunted look. He was eager for the end of the experiment. Meanwhile, The Thinking Machine was up to his old tricks. He threw another piece of cloth to the guard outside, bearing the words *Only two days more*.

On the sixth day, the warden received a letter stating that Dr. Ransome and Mr. Fielding would be at Chisholm Prison on the following evening. In case Professor Van Dusen had not yet escaped, they would meet him there.

In case he had not yet escaped! The warden smiled grimly. Escaped!

On the afternoon of the seventh day, the warden passed Cell 13 and glanced in. The Thinking Machine was lying on the iron bed, apparently sleeping lightly. The cell looked exactly as it always did. It was then 4:00 PM. The warden would swear that no man was going to leave Cell 13 in the next four hours.

That evening at 6:00 PM, he saw the guard.

"Everything all right in Cell 13?" he asked.

"Yes, sir," replied the guard.

The warden felt relieved when he greeted Dr. Ransome and Mr. Fielding at 7:00 PM. Just then, the guard from the river side of the prison yard entered the office.

"The arc light on my side of the yard won't light," the guard reported.

"Confound it!" thundered the warden. "Everything has happened since that man's been here."

The guard went back to his post in the darkness, and the warden phoned the electric company.

"This is Chisholm Prison," he said. "Send three or four men down here at once to fix an arc light."

The warden hung up and went into the prison yard. While Dr. Ransome and Mr. Fielding sat waiting, the guard at the outer gate came in with a special delivery letter and put it on the warden's desk.

It was nearly 8:00 PM when the warden returned to his office. The electricians had arrived and were now at work. The warden pressed a button to communicate with the man at the outer gate in the wall.

"How many electricians came in?" he asked. "Four? All right, be certain that only four go out. That's all."

The warden noticed the special delivery letter on his desk. As he ripped open the envelope, he said, "Gentlemen, I want to report to you something about how — Great Caesar!" he ended suddenly as he read the letter. He sat open-mouthed with astonishment.

"What is it?" asked Fielding.

"A special delivery letter from Cell 13," gasped the warden. "An invitation to supper."

"What?" The other two stood up, unbelieving.

The warden called sharply to a guard outside in the corridor. "Run down to Cell 13 and see if that man's in there."

The guard left at once. Then Dr. Ransome and Mr. Fielding examined the letter. "It's the Professor's handwriting. There's no question of that," said Dr. Ransome.

Just then a buzz sounded on the telephone from the outer gate. The warden, still dazed, picked up the receiver.

"Hello! Two reporters, eh? Let 'em come in." He turned suddenly to Dr. Ransome and Mr. Fielding. "The man can't be out. He must be in his cell."

At that moment, the guard returned. "He's still in his cell, sir," he reported. "He's lying down."

"There, I told you so," said the warden. He drew a deep breath. "But how did he mail that letter?"

There was a rap on the steel door which led from the jail yard into the warden's office.

"It's the reporters," said the warden. "Let them in," he instructed the guard. "Don't say anything about this in front of them," he told the other two men. "I'd never hear the end of it."

The door opened, and two men entered. "Good evening, gentlemen," said one of the newcomers. His name was Hutchinson Hatch; the warden knew him well.

"Well," said the other man sharply. "Here I am."

It was The Thinking Machine! He squinted at the warden, who sat down as if his legs had collapsed under him. Dr. Ransome and Mr. Fielding were amazed, too.

"How — how — how did you do it?" the warden finally managed to gasp.

"Come back to the cell," said The Thinking Machine.

The warden, almost in a trance, led the way. He flashed his light in the cell. There seemed to be nothing unusual. There on the bed lay the figure of the Professor. There was the bushy hair! The warden wondered if he could be dreaming. With trembling hands, he unlocked the cell door, and they entered.

The Thinking Machine kicked at the steel bars in the bottom of the cell door, and three bars were pushed out of place. A fourth bar broke off and rolled away in the corridor.

Then the prisoner stood on the bed to reach the small window. He swept his hand across the opening, and every bar came out.

"What's this in the bed?" demanded the warden, who was slowly recovering.

"A wig," was the reply. "Turn down the covers."

The warden did so. Beneath the covers lay a large coil of strong rope, a dagger, three files, ten feet of wire, a hammer, and a pair of steel pliers.

"How did you do it?" demanded the warden.

"You gentlemen have an appointment for supper with me at 9:30," said The Thinking Machine. "Come on, or we'll be late."

The guests at Professor Van Dusen's supper party were Dr. Ransome, Albert Fielding, the warden, and Hutchinson Hatch, the reporter. When the meal was nearly finished, The Thinking Machine turned to Dr. Ransome and demanded, "Do you believe it now?"

"I do," replied Dr. Ransome.

"Do you admit it was a fair test?"

"I do. Suppose you tell us how you did it?"

The Thinking Machine began the story.

"My agreement was," he began, "to go into a cell with nothing except my clothes and to leave that cell within a week. I had never seen Chisholm Prison. When I went into the cell, I asked for tooth powder, one five- and two ten-dollar bills, and to have my shoes polished. You agreed to these requests.

"The next morning, after breakfast, I examined the outside surroundings from my cell window. One look told me it would be useless to try to scale the wall.

"From this first look, I knew the river was on this side of the prison, and that there was a playground. I knew, then, one important thing — that anyone might approach the prison wall from this side without attracting any special attention.

"But the thing that caught *my* attention was the wire to the arc light; it ran within a few feet of my cell window. That was useful to know in case I found it necessary to cut off that arc light."

"Oh, you shut it off tonight, then?" asked the warden.

The Thinking Machine went on without answering the question. "I considered the idea of escaping through the prison building. I recalled just how I had come into the cell. Seven doors lay between me and the outside. So, for the time being, I gave up the idea of escaping that way."

The Thinking Machine paused. For a moment, there was silence. Then the scientist went on:

"While I was thinking about these things, a rat ran across my foot. It suggested a new line of thought. There were at least a half-dozen rats in the cell — I could see their beady eyes. Yet, I had noticed none coming under the cell door. I

frightened them purposely and watched the cell door to see if they went out that way. They did not, but they were gone. Obviously, they went another way. Another way meant another opening.

"I searched for this opening and found it. It was an old drainpipe, partly choked with dirt and dust. Drainpipes must lead outside the prison grounds. This one probably led to the river, or near it. So the rats must have come from that direction.

"When the guard came with my lunch, he told me two important things, although he didn't know it. One was that a new system of plumbing had been put in the prison seven years before; another was that the river was only 300 feet away. Then I knew positively that the drainpipe was part of an old system. I knew, too, that it slanted toward the river.

"The first thing was to make the warden think I was trying to communicate with you, Dr. Ransome. So I wrote a note on a piece of cloth I tore from my shirt, addressed it to you, tied a five-dollar bill around it, and threw it out the window. I knew the guard would take it to the warden. Do you have that first note, warden?"

The warden produced the coded message: *Epa cseot d'net niiy awe htto n'si sih "T."*

"Read it backward, beginning with the "T" signature, and ignore the breaks between words," the Professor directed.

The warden studied the message and then read the following: " 'This is not the way I intend to escape.' What did you write with?" asked the warden.

"This," said The Thinking Machine, and he stuck out his shoe. It was the shoe he had worn in prison, though the polish was gone — scraped off clean. "The shoe polish, moistened with water, was my ink; the metal tip of the shoelace made a fairly good pen."

"You're a wonder," said the warden admiringly. "Go on."

"That set off a search of my cell," said The Thinking Machine. "I wanted to get the warden into the habit of searching my cell and finding nothing so that he would get disgusted and quit.

"Then he took my white shirt away and gave me a prison shirt. He was satisfied that those two pieces of the shirt were all that were missing. But while he was searching my cell, I had another piece of that same shirt, about nine inches square, rolled into a small ball in my mouth."

"Nine inches of that shirt?" demanded the warden. "Where did it come from?"

"The fronts of all stiff white shirts have a triple layer," was the reply. "I tore out the inside layer, leaving only two layers. I knew you wouldn't see it. So much for that.

"Then I took my first serious step toward freedom," said Professor Van Dusen. "I knew that the drainpipe led somewhere around the playground outside. I knew that rats came into my cell from out there. Could I communicate with someone outside?

"I realized that the first thing I needed was thread." He stopped to roll up his trouser legs and showed that the tops of both socks were gone. "I unraveled these tops, and I had about a quarter of a mile of strong thread I could depend on.

"Then, on half the cloth I had left, I wrote a letter to Hutchinson Hatch—I knew he would be interested in a good newspaper story. I tied a ten-dollar bill to the letter, so someone would be sure to pick it up. I wrote on the cloth: 'Finder of this, deliver to Hutchinson Hatch, *Daily American,* who will give another ten dollars for the information.'

"The next thing was to get this note outside near the playground, where a child might find it. I took one of the rats, tied the cloth and money firmly to one leg, fastened my thread to another leg, and turned him loose in the drainpipe. I reasoned that the rat's fear would make him run until he was outside the pipe and then, once outside, he would stop to gnaw off the cloth and money.

"From the moment the rat disappeared into the dusty pipe, I became anxious. I was taking so many chances. A thousand things might have gone wrong. But after a long wait, only a few feet of string remained in my cell; that made me think the rat was outside the pipe. Now the question was: Would the note reach Mr. Hatch?

"This done, I took some other steps. I tried openly to bribe my guard. Then I did something else to make the warden nervous. I took the steel supports out of the heels of my shoes and made a show of sawing the bars of my cell window. The warden began shaking the bars of my cell window to see if they were tight. They were then.

"I had some nervous hours waiting to see what would happen to my plan. I didn't sleep that night for fear that I would miss the signal that Mr. Hatch had received my note — the twitch of the thread. At about 3:30, I felt the twitch in the pipe, and no prisoner ever welcomed anything more."

The Thinking Machine stopped and turned to the reporter. "You'd better explain what you did," he said.

"The cloth note was brought to me by a boy who had been playing baseball," Hatch said. "I immediately saw a big story in it, so I gave the boy another ten dollars and got several spools of silk thread, some twine, and a roll of thin wire. The Professor's note suggested that I have the finder of the note show me where it was picked up, and told me to make my search from there. If I found the other end of the thread, I was to twitch it gently three times, then a fourth.

"After an hour and 20 minutes of searching, I found the end of the drainpipe, half hidden in weeds. The pipe was very large there, about 12 inches across. I found the end of the thread, twitched it four times, and got back a twitch from the other end.

"Then I fastened the silk to the thread, and when that had been pulled in, I tied on

the twine, and then wire. Then we had a good line, which rats couldn't gnaw, from the end of the drain into the cell."

The Thinking Machine raised his hand and Hatch stopped.

"All this was done in absolute silence," he said, "but when the wire reached my hand, I could have shouted for joy. Then I used the pipe as a speaking tube. Neither of us could hear very clearly, but I dared not speak loud. At last I made him understand what I wanted.

"I asked for nitric acid, and I repeated the word 'acid' several times. Then I heard a shriek from a cell above me. I knew instantly that someone had overheard. If you had entered my cell at that moment, warden, my whole plan of escape would have ended."

"That was Joseph Ballard, a prisoner, who cried out," said the warden. "He had been accused of throwing acid in a woman's face. When he heard the word 'acid' in a ghostly voice, he got scared, and confessed. Now I see," he continued, "how you got things in your cell through the pipe. But how did you hide them?"

"I merely dropped them back into the pipe. You, warden, could not have reached the connecting wire with your fingers; they are too large. My fingers, as you see, are longer and more slender. Besides, I guarded the opening of that pipe with a rat — you remember how."

"I remember," said the warden.

"Mr. Hatch could not send me anything

useful through the pipe until the next night," the scientist continued, "although he did send me change for ten dollars as a test. Then I planned the method of escape.

"On the last day of my imprisonment, when it was dark, I planned to cut the wire to the arc light, which was only a few feet from my window. I could reach it with an acid-tipped wire I had. That would make that side of the prison perfectly dark while the electricians were looking for the break. That would also bring Mr. Hatch into the prison yard.

"The work of cutting the steel bars of the window and door was fairly easy with nitric acid, which I got through the pipe in thin bottles. Still, it took time. The guard below looked at me as I worked on the window bars with the acid on a piece of wire. I used the tooth powder to prevent the acid from spreading. I looked away as I worked, and each minute the acid cut deeper into the metal. I noticed that the guards always tried the door by shaking the upper part of the bars, never the lower ones. So I cut the lower bars, leaving them in place with thin strips of metal."

The Thinking Machine sat silent for several minutes. "I think that makes everything clear. Whatever things I have not explained were done to confuse the warden and guards. I put the rope and the other things in my bed to please Mr. Hatch, who wanted to improve the story. Of course, the wig was necessary in my plan. I wrote the special delivery letter in my cell with Mr. Hatch's pen, then sent it out to him and he mailed it. That's all, I think."

"But how did you ever leave the prison grounds and come in through the gate to my office?" asked the warden.

"Perfectly simple," said the scientist. "I cut the electric-light wire with acid when the current was off. Then, when the current was turned on, the arc didn't light. When the guard went to tell you, I crept out the window—it was a tight fit—replaced the bars by standing on a narrow ledge, and stayed in the shadows until the electricians arrived. Mr. Hatch was one of them.

"When he saw me, he handed me a cap and a shirt and pants, which I put on in the yard, within ten feet of you, warden. We then went out to the electric company's truck outside the gate. We changed our clothes and returned, asking to see you. We saw you. That's all."

There was silence for several minutes. Dr. Ransome was the first to speak. "Wonderful!" he exclaimed. "Perfectly amazing."

"How did Mr. Hatch happen to come with the electricians?" asked Fielding.

"His father is manager of the company," The Thinking Machine replied.

"Suppose — just suppose there had been no old plumbing system and no drainpipe?" asked the warden curiously.

"There is always a way out," said The Thinking Machine with a puzzling smile. "Don't ever think you can hold anybody with a good mind." ◆

READING CHECK

Answer the following questions about "The Thinking Machine, Part 2." You may look back at the story if you want to.

1. What puzzled the warden most about the third piece of cloth The Thinking Machine sent down to the guard? What did the warden do with the piece of cloth?

2. When the warden discovered the round hole in the floor of Cell 13, what was the first thing he did? What surprise did he get?

3. What message was in the special delivery letter from The Thinking Machine to the warden? What proof was offered to the warden that the letter was really written by The Thinking Machine?

4. How did the warden react when The Thinking Machine and the newspaper reporter turned up in his office? What did the warden say? How did he say it? Until that moment, where did he think The Thinking Machine was?

5. What did The Thinking Machine explain at his supper party?

6. What one question did the warden still have after all the details of the escape were explained? How did The Thinking Machine answer that question?

WHAT DO YOU THINK?

1. What do you think was the most important factor in the success of The Thinking Machine's escape? Why?

2. The newspaper reporter helped The Thinking Machine because he thought the prison experiment would make a good news story. Do you think that readers would believe the story? Why, or why not? Do you think all, or some, of the events in the story could really happen? Explain your answer.

3. If you could think up a challenge for The Thinking Machine what would it be? Do you think he could solve the problem? Explain why or why not.

VOCABULARY CHECK

Read the following sentences and choose the correct meaning of each word in **bold print.** Then write each word and its meaning on your paper.

1. The professor **moistened** the polish on his shoes to make ink.

    (wet, scraped)

2. In a **trance,** the stunned warden led the way.
    (state of anger, sleep-like state)

3. The guard **immediately** put the special delivery letter on the warden's desk.
    (instantly, thoughtfully)

4. When the **current** was turned on, the lights didn't work.
    (switch, electricity)

5. **Twine** and wire were used to make a line from the drain to the cell.
    (strong string, heavy steel)

STRATEGY CHECK

The paragraph below is based on the story "The Thinking Machine, Part 2." Choose a word that makes sense to fill in each blank. Use the rest of the paragraph and what you remember about the story to help you. Then write the whole paragraph on your paper.

On the fourth day of the experiment, The Thinking Machine spent a lot of time looking out the ____ of his cell. On the fifth and sixth ____, he kept up his old tricks. On the seventh day — the last day of the experiment — the warden got a special delivery ____ from The Thinking Machine. Next, a ____ reporter and The Thinking Machine himself showed up in the warden's office. The Thinking Machine — once again a free man — had proved that by ____, it's possible to get out of the tightest of tight spots.

"POEMS ABOUT TIGHT SPOTS"

The three poems that you will read here talk about different kinds of animals. The first two, "The Shark" and "A Narrow Fellow in the Grass," describe dangerous animals. The third, "Be Like the Bird," uses an animal as an example

WORDS TO KNOW

The words in **bold print** are from "Poems About Tight Spots." Study each word and its meaning carefully.

I stooped to **secure** the snake.
   secure — take hold of

The shark is **treacherous.**
   treacherous — sly and dangerous

The shark's self control is **astounding.**
   astounding — amazing, very surprising

THE SHARK

by LORD ALFRED DOUGLAS

A treacherous monster is the Shark,
He never makes the least remark.

And when he sees you on the sand,
He doesn't seem to want to land.

His eyes do not grow bright or roll,
He has astounding self-control.

And when towards the sea you leap,
He looks as if he were asleep.

But when you once get in his range,
His whole demeanor seems to change.

He throws his body right about,
And his true character comes out.

It's no use crying or appealing,
He seems to lose all decent feeling.

After this warning you will wish
To keep clear of this treacherous fish.

His back is black, his stomach white,
He has a very dangerous bite.

A NARROW FELLOW IN THE GRASS

by EMILY DICKINSON

A narrow fellow in the grass
Occasionally rides;
You may have met him,
   —did you not?
His notice sudden is.

The grass divides as with a
   comb,
A spotted shaft is seen;
And then it closes at your
   feet
And opens further on.

He likes a boggy acre,
A floor too cool for corn.
Yet when a child, and barefoot,
I more than once, at morn,

Have passed, I thought, a
   whip-lash
Unbraiding in the sun,—
When, stooping to secure it,
It wrinkled, and was gone.

Several of nature's people
I know, and they know me;
I feel for them a transport
Of cordiality;

But never met this fellow,
Attended or alone,
Without a tighter breathing,
And zero at the bone.

BE LIKE THE BIRD

by VICTOR HUGO

Be like the bird, who
Halting in his flight
On limb too slight
Feels it give way beneath him,
Yet sings
Knowing he hath wings.

WHAT DO YOU THINK?

1. Does the author of the poem "The Shark" want to scare the reader? Do you agree with the things he says about sharks? Explain your answer.

2. Emily Dickinson had a very original way of expressing her ideas. Many people would describe being frightened by a snake, by saying "I was so frightened, I felt chilled to the bone." What does Emily Dickinson say instead?

3. Birds have wings, but people do not. What does it mean for a person to know that he or she "has wings?"

VOCABULARY CHECK

Read the following sentences and choose the correct meaning of each word in **bold print.** Then write each word and its meaning on your paper.

1. The **treacherous** shark swam below.
   (sly and dangerous, fast and powerful)

2. The shark showed **astounding** self control.
   (slight, amazing)

3. It was difficult to **secure** the snake.
   (follow, take hold of)

READING REVIEW

Tight Spots is all about people dealing with difficult or dangerous situations. Complete the following sentences about the selections in the unit. Choose the best ending for each sentence. Then write the complete sentences on your paper.

1. In "He Was A Good Lion," Beryl tried not to act afraid in front of the lion because ___ .
   a. Singh told her to be brave
   b. lions do not like cowards
   c. her friends might find out
   d. she was too scared to think

2. In "He Was A Good Lion," Paddy's behavior proves that ___ .
   a. lions can make good pets
   b. no lion is really tame
   c. a starving lion will attack a human
   d. lions like fresh meat

3. In "Buried Treasure," Speed was finally ___ .
   a. dug out of the sand
   b. arrested for disturbing the peace
   c. picked up by a rocket
   d. punished by his mother

4. In "The Thinking Machine, Part 1," the Professor studied every inch of his cell to find ___ .
   a. out about other prisoners
   b. clues to plan his escape
   c. something to write on
   d. scraps of food to eat

5. In "The Thinking Machine, Part 2," the Professor tells that he used a rat to ___ .
   a. make trouble at the prison
   b. be his pet
   c. pretend he was insane
   d. carry a message

6. In "The Thinking Machine, Part 2," The Professor has a supper party where he proves his point that a good mind ___ .
   a. still feels fear
   b. can make ink from shoe polish
   c. is the best helper in a tight spot
   d. is the hope of the future

VOCABULARY REVIEW

Review some words that describe tight spots. Choose a word from the list to replace the words in **bold print** in each sentence below. Then write the completed sentences on your paper.

squinted   **scuttled**   **nudged**
suspicious   **distinguished**

1. Professor Van Dusen was the prison's most **famous** inmate.

2. A crab **ran quickly** forward.

3. Clarence **gently pushed** Brian to let him know he was there.

4. Speed was **untrusting** of Clarence's ability to find buried treasure.

5. The Lion **looked with slightly closed eyes** at Beryl.

WRITING ABOUT TIGHT SPOTS

1. Choose one of the characters in the unit who found himself or herself in a tight spot. You may choose Speed, Beryl, or The Thinking Machine. Imagine that you are that person helping a newspaper or magazine reporter to write a story about your adventure. Write two or three paragraphs about some of the events that led to your getting in a tight spot. Describe what you did to handle the situtation. Finally, write about your feelings afterward.

2. Use an encyclopedia and other library resources to find out more about lions and how they behave in the wild. Make a list of the facts you find.

3. What quality do you think is most helpful when you find yourself in a tight spot? Is it cleverness, bravery, or the ability to keep calm? Using examples from the stories you've read, write at least one paragraph to explain your answer.

◆ GLOSSARY ◆

Here are the words that you have studied in this book, with their pronunciations and meanings. Remember, sometimes a word can have more than one meaning. The meanings listed here fit the way the words are used in the selections.

PRONUNCIATION KEY

ă	pat	h	hat	ŏ	pot	t	tight
ā	pay, aid	hw	which	ō	go, coat	th	thin, path
â	care, air	ĭ	pit	ô	for, paw	th	this, bathe
ä	father, art	ī	kind, pie	oi	oil, boy	ŭ	cut, rough
b	bib	î	fierce, deer	ou	out, cow	û	turn, firm
ch	church	j	judge, giant	ŏŏ	look	v	vine, cave
d	deed	k	kick, cook	ōō	boot, suit	w	with
ě	pet, pleasure	l	lid, needle	p	pop	y	yes
ē	bee, easy	m	mum, am	r	roar	z	zebra, rose
f	fast, off	n	no, sudden	s	see, sauce	zh	vision
g	gag	ng	thing	sh	ship, action	ə	about, silent

This pronunciation key will help you pronounce each glossary word. Here is an example:

for·tune /fôr′ chən/ Good or bad luck

The letters and symbols between slashes (/) stand for the sounds in the word *fortune*. The stress mark (′) shows that the first syllable is "accented," or spoken with more force. The symbol "ə," which is called a *schwa,* stands for a very light "uh" sound.

a·ban·doned /ə băn′ dənd/ Deserted
a·broad /ə brôd′/ In a foreign land
ac·cent /ăk′ sěnt/ Manner of speaking
ac·com·plished /ə kŏm′ plĭsht/ Completed
a·cre /ā′ kər/ 43,560 square feet
af·fec·tion /ə fěk′ shən/ Fondness, love
aim·less·ly /ām′ lĭs lē/ Without purpose
a·loof·ness /ə lōōf′ nĭs/ Coolness of manner
anx·ious·ly /ăngk′ shəs lē/ In a worried way
as·cend·ing /ə sěn′ dĭng/ Rising
a·ston·ished /ə stŏn′ ĭsht/ Amazed
a·stound·ing /ə stoun′ dĭng/ Amazing
at·las /ăt′ ləs/ Book of maps

barge /bärj/ Enter without warning
be·grudge /bĭ grŭj′/ Give unwillinging

be·wil·dered /bĭ wĭl′ dərd/ Puzzled
bil·lows /bĭl′ ōz/ Waves
bi·o·log·i·cal /bī ə lŏj′ ĭ kəl/ Having to do with the science of living things
bi·ol·o·gists /bī ŏl′ ə jĭsts/ Scientists who study animals and plants
bleak /blēk/ Cold and gloomy
blurt·ed /blûr′ tĭd/ Spoke suddenly

cam·ou·flage /kăm′ ə fläzh/ Disguise
ca·reen·ing /kə rēn′ ĭng/ Tilting, lurching
cem·e·ter·y /sěm′ ə tĕr ē/ Graveyard
cer·e·mo·ny /sěr′ ə mō nē/ A formal event
cer·tif·i·cate /sər tĭf′ ĭ kĭt/ Document
chal·leng·er /chăl′ ən jər/ Rival
cir·cum·stance /sûr′ kəm stăns/ Event
cleav·ing /klē′ vĭng/ Splitting apart

co·in·ci·dence /kō ĭn′ sə dəns/ Things happening together, by chance

com·mon·ly /kŏm′ ən lē/ Usually

com·pan·ions /kəm păn′ yənz/ Those who spend time together

con·cen·trat·ing /kŏn′ sən trā tĭng/ Fixing attention

con·done /kən dōn′/ Agree with

con·fi·dent /kŏn′ fə dənt/ Certain

con·stant·ly /kŏn′ stənt lē/ Always

con·temp·tu·ous /kən tĕmp′ choo əs/ Scornful

con·tent·ment /kən tĕnt′ mənt/ Satisfaction

co·or·di·na·tion /kō ôr də nā′ shən/ Smooth movement

cope /kōp/ Deal with

cor·ri·dor /kôr′ ĭ dər/ Hallway

craft·i·ness /krăf′ tē nĭs/ Slyness

crammed /krămd/ Packed full

cry·stal /krĭs′ təl/ Glass cover on a watch

cul·ti·vate /kŭl′ tə vāt/ Break up (soil)

cur·rent /kûr′ ənt/ Electricity

dart·ing /där′ tĭng/ Moving quickly

daw·dling /dôd′ lĭng/ Moving too slowly

de·ci·phered /dĭ sī′ fərd/ Figured out

de·fi·ance /dĭ fī′ əns/ Willful disobedience

de·scent /dĭ sĕnt′/ Fall

de·sert·ed /dĭ zûr′ tĭd/ Left

des·ti·na·tion /dĕs tə nā′ shən/ Goal

dic·ta·tor·ship /dĭk tā′ tər shĭp/ Country ruled by one all-powerful person

dis·crim·i·nat·ing /dĭs krĭm′ ə nā tĭng/ Treating differently and unfairly

dis·grun·tled /dĭs grŭn′ təld/ Annoyed

dis·tin·guished /dĭs tĭng′ gwĭsht/ Famous

dread·ful /drĕd′ fəl/ Terrible

drift·er /drĭf′ tər/ A wanderer

dune /doon/ Hill of sand on a beach

eaves /ēvz/ The lower edges of a roof

e·lim·i·nat·ing /ĭ lĭm′ ə nā tĭng/ Removing

el·o·quent·ly /ĕl′ ə kwənt lē/ Movingly

em·braced /ĕm brāst′/ Hugged

en·tice /ĕn tīs′/ Tempt

ep·i·dem·ic /ep ə dĕm′ ĭk/ Fast spreading of a disease to many people

es·cort·ed /ĕs kôr′ tĭd/ Accompanied

es·sayed /ĕ sād′/ Tried, attempted

ev·i·dence /ĕv′ ə dəns/ Proof

ex·ag·ger·ate /ĕg zăj′ ə rāt/ Portray a thing as greater than it really is

ex·ot·ic /ĕg zŏt′ ĭk/ Interestingly different

ex·plod·ed /ĕk splō′ dəd/ Said angrily

ex·plore /ĕk splôr′/ Travel to discover

fac·ul·ty /făk′ əl tē/ Teaching staff

fam·ine /făm′ ĭn/ Great lack of food

fier·y /fīr′ ē/ Like fire

fil·ter /fĭl′ tər/ Strain out (e.g., dirt)

fla·min·go /flə mĭng′ gō/ Large bird

flex /flĕks/ Bend

frag·ile /frăj′ əl/ Easily broken

glare /glâr/ Fierce, angry look

glob·al /glō′ bəl/ Of the whole world

guard·ians /gär′ dē ənz/ Protectors

har·vest /här′ vĕst/ To gather in a crop

haze /hāz/ Light "fog" of dust and smoke

heart·i·ness /här′ tē nĭs/ Enthusiasm

heir·looms /âr′ loomz/ Things inherited

hi·bis·cus /hī bĭs′ kəs/ A flowering plant

ho·ri·zon /hə rī′ zən/ The line where earth and sky seem to meet

hy·dro·pon·ics /hī drə pŏn′ ĭks/ The science of growing plants in water

ig·nore /ĭg nôr′/ Not notice

im·me·di·ate·ly /ĭ mē′ dē ĭt lē/ Instantly

im·pa·tient /ĭm pā′ shənt/ Annoyed at delay

in·dig·nant /ĭn dĭg′ nənt/ Justly angered

in·fe·ri·or /ĭn fîr′ ē ər/ Of poor quality

in·quis·i·tive /ĭn kwĭz′ ə tĭv/ Curious

in·se·cure /ĭn sĭ kyoor′/ Not sure or safe

in·sis·tent /ĭn sĭs′ tənt/ Firm; determined

in·trud·er /ĭn troo′ dər/ Uninvited guest

in·ves·ti·gate /ĭn vĕs′ tĭ gāt/ Find out about

i·ron·ic /ī rŏn′ ĭk/ Contrary to expectation

la·crosse /lə krôs′/ A ball game

lank·y /lăng′ kē/ Tall and thin

le·git·i·mate /lə jĭt′ ə mĭt/ Lawful

le·nien·cy /lē′ nē ən sē/ Gentleness

lev·ee /lĕv′ ē/ Landing place on a river

lic·o·rice /lĭk′ ər ĭs/ or /lĭk′ ər ĭsh/ A candy

lim·ou·sine /lĭm ə zēn′/ Large automobile

man·tle /măn′ təl/ Coat or cloak

men·ace /mĕn′ ĭs/ Threat of danger

me·te·or·ites /mē′ tē ə rīts/ Lumps of metal or stone that fall from space to the earth

mi·grate /mī′ grāt/ Travel

min·gled /mǐng′ gəld/ Mixed together

mois·tened /mois′ ənd/ Wet

moored /mŏord/ Tied up

muf·fled /mŭf′ əld/ Hard to hear

mur·mur /mûr′ mər/ Soft sound

mus·cu·lar /mŭs′ kyə lər/ Powerful

mys·te·ri·ous·ly /mǐ stîr′ ē əs lē/ Unexplainably

nav·i·ga·tion /năv ə gā′ shən/ Traveling a route

nec·tar /něk′ tər/ Sweet juice from flowers

ne·glect·ed /nǐ glěk′ tǐd/ Left without care

nick·el /nǐk′ əl/ A hard metal

nim·ble /nǐm′ bəl/ Quick and light

no·ti·fied /nō′ tə fīd/ Told, informed

nudged /nŭjd/ Pushed gently

ob·serv·ing /əb zûr′ vǐng/ Watching

off·spring /ôf′ sprǐng/ Children

op·ti·cian /ŏp tǐsh′ ən/ Maker of eyeglasses

ox·y·gen /ŏk′ sǐ jən/ A gas found in air

pe·des·tri·ans /pə děs′ trē ənz/ Walkers

pen·al·ty /pěn′ əl tē/ Fine or punishment

pet·ri·fied /pět′ rə fīd/ Frozen with fear

pho·to·gen·ic /fō tə jěn′ ĭk/ Looking good in photographs

pierc·ing /pîr′ sǐng/ Sharp, cutting

plowed /ploud/ Used a tool to break up soil

pos·sess·ing /pə zěs′ ǐng/ Owning

prac·ti·ca·ble /prăk′ tǐ kə bəl/ Practical

pre·cau·tion /prǐ kô′ shən/ Care taken to avoid danger

pre·lim·i·nar·ies /prǐ lǐm′ ə něr ēz/ Tryouts

pre·sid·ed /prǐ zī′ dǐd/ Was in charge

prompt /prŏmpt/ On time

prun·ing shears /prōōn′ ǐng shîrz/ Tool for cutting branches of trees and bushes

pyr·a·mids /pîr′ ə mǐdz/ Huge buildings with triangular sides

re·form /rǐ fôrm′/ Change bad behavior

re·li·a·ble /rǐ lī′ ə bəl/ Dependable

re·mark·a·ble /rǐ mär′ kə bəl/ Unusual

rep·li·ca /rěp′ lə kə/ An exact copy

re·sem·blance /rǐ zěm′ bləns/ Likeness

re·sist /rǐ zǐst′/ Fight against

re·spond·ed /rǐ spŏn′ dǐd/ Reacted

re·strain /rǐ strān′/ Hold back

re·veal /rǐ vēl′/ Make known

rhyme /rīm/ Poem

roamed /rōmd/ Wandered around

scale /skāl/ To climb

scav·eng·ing /skăv′ ǐn jǐng/ Searching

scut·tled /skŭt′ əld/ Ran quickly

se·cure /sǐ kyŏor′/ Take hold of

se·vere /sə vîr′/ Very harsh

shep·herd·ing /shěp′ ər dǐng/ Guiding

shift·ed /shǐf′ tǐd/ Moved

shin·gle /shǐng′ gəl/ Gravel-covered beach

skit·tish /skǐt′ ǐsh/ Nervous

snick·ered /snǐk′ ərd/ Laughed snidely

sol·i·tud·i·nous /sŏl ə tōō′ də nəs/ Lonely

spar·ring /spär′ ǐng/ Boxing practice

spec·tac·u·lar /spěk tăk′ yə lər/ Amazing

sprawled /sprôld/ Stretched out

sprint·ed /sprǐn′ tǐd/ Ran quickly

spurred /spûrd/ Encouraged

squint·ed /skwǐn′ tǐd/ Narrowed the eyes

stalk·ing /stô′ kǐng/ Following like a hunter

strides /strīdz/ Big, energetic steps

su·prem·a·cy /sə prěm′ ə sē/ Being the best

surge /sûrj/ Strong, sudden increase

sur·plus /sûr′ pləs/ Extra

sus·pi·cious /sə spǐsh′ əs/ Not trusting

Swa·hi·li /swä hē′ lē/ An African language

tar·pau·lin /tär pô′ lǐn/ Waterproof sheet

tire·some /tīr′ səm/ Annoying, boring

tour·na·ment /tŏor′ nə mənt/ Contests

trance /trăns/ A state almost like sleep

treach·er·ous /trěch′ ər əs/ Dangerous

twi·light /twī′ līt/ Dusk

twine /twīn/ A strong string

un·com·mon·ly /ŭn kŏm′ ən lē/ Unusually

u·nique /yōō nēk′/ Like no other

un·ruf·fled /ŭn rŭf′ əld/ Not disturbed

van·ished /văn′ ǐsht/ Disappeared

vi·tal /vī′ təl/ Very important

vol·un·tar·i·ly /vŏl ən târ′ ə lē/ By choice

wal·low·ing /wŏl′ ō ǐng/ Rolling about

wan·der·lust /wŏn′ dər lŭst/ Desire to roam

wis·dom /wǐz′ dəm/ Great understanding